Fluency in Number Facts

Years 5 & 6

Peter Clarke

William Collins' dream of knowledge for all began with the publication of his first book in 1819. A self-educated mill worker, he not only enriched millions of lives, but also founded a flourishing publishing house. Today, staying true to this spirit, Collins books are packed with inspiration, innovation and practical expertise. They place you at the centre of a world of possibility and give you exactly what you need to explore it.

Collins. Freedom to teach.

Published by Collins

An imprint of HarperCollins*Publishers*
77–85 Fulham Palace Road
Hammersmith
London
W6 8JB

Browse the complete Collins catalogue at
www.collins.co.uk

© HarperCollins*Publishers* Limited 2013

10 9 8 7 6 5 4 3 2 1

ISBN-978-0-00-753132-5

The authors assert their moral rights to be identified as the authors of this work

British Library Cataloguing in Publication Data
A Catalogue record for this publication is available from the British Library

Edited by Gaynor Spry
Cover design by Nikki Kenwood
Cover artwork by Gwyneth Williams
Internal design by Nikki Kenwood
Illustrations by Fran Brylewska and Jouve
Typeset by Jouve

Printed by L.E.G.O. S.p.A. - Italy

Acknowledgement
The author wishes to thank Brian Molyneaux for his valuable contribution to this publication.

Contents

Addition and subtraction number facts to 20

Number facts for 0

$0 + 0 = 0$ | $0 - 0 = 0$

Number facts for 1

$1 + 0 = 1$ | $1 - 0 = 1$
$0 + 1 = 1$ | $1 - 1 = 0$

Number facts for 2

$2 + 0 = 2$ | $2 - 0 = 2$
$1 + 1 = 2$ | $2 - 1 = 1$
$0 + 2 = 2$ | $2 - 2 = 0$

Number facts for 3

$3 + 0 = 3$ | $3 - 0 = 3$
$2 + 1 = 3$ | $3 - 1 = 2$
$1 + 2 = 3$ | $3 - 2 = 1$
$0 + 3 = 3$ | $3 - 3 = 0$

Number facts for 4

$4 + 0 = 4$ | $4 - 0 = 4$
$3 + 1 = 4$ | $4 - 1 = 3$
$2 + 2 = 4$ | $4 - 2 = 2$
$1 + 3 = 4$ | $4 - 3 = 1$
$0 + 4 = 4$ | $4 - 4 = 0$

Number facts for 5

$5 + 0 = 5$ | $5 - 0 = 5$
$4 + 1 = 5$ | $5 - 1 = 4$
$3 + 2 = 5$ | $5 - 2 = 3$
$2 + 3 = 5$ | $5 - 3 = 2$
$1 + 4 = 5$ | $5 - 4 = 1$
$0 + 5 = 5$ | $5 - 5 = 0$

Number facts for 6

$6 + 0 = 6$ | $6 - 0 = 6$
$5 + 1 = 6$ | $6 - 1 = 5$
$4 + 2 = 6$ | $6 - 2 = 4$
$3 + 3 = 6$ | $6 - 3 = 3$
$2 + 4 = 6$ | $6 - 4 = 2$
$1 + 5 = 6$ | $6 - 5 = 1$
$0 + 6 = 6$ | $6 - 6 = 0$

Number facts for 7

$7 + 0 = 7$ | $7 - 0 = 7$
$6 + 1 = 7$ | $7 - 1 = 6$
$5 + 2 = 7$ | $7 - 2 = 5$
$4 + 3 = 7$ | $7 - 3 = 4$
$3 + 4 = 7$ | $7 - 4 = 3$
$2 + 5 = 7$ | $7 - 5 = 2$
$1 + 6 = 7$ | $7 - 6 = 1$
$0 + 7 = 7$ | $7 - 7 = 0$

Number facts for 8

$8 + 0 = 8$ | $8 - 0 = 8$
$7 + 1 = 8$ | $8 - 1 = 7$
$6 + 2 = 8$ | $8 - 2 = 6$
$5 + 3 = 8$ | $8 - 3 = 5$
$4 + 4 = 8$ | $8 - 4 = 4$
$3 + 5 = 8$ | $8 - 5 = 3$
$2 + 6 = 8$ | $8 - 6 = 2$
$1 + 7 = 8$ | $8 - 7 = 1$
$0 + 8 = 8$ | $8 - 8 = 0$

Number facts for 9

$9 + 0 = 9$ | $9 - 0 = 9$
$8 + 1 = 9$ | $9 - 1 = 8$
$7 + 2 = 9$ | $9 - 2 = 7$
$6 + 3 = 9$ | $9 - 3 = 6$
$5 + 4 = 9$ | $9 - 4 = 5$
$4 + 5 = 9$ | $9 - 5 = 4$
$3 + 6 = 9$ | $9 - 6 = 3$
$2 + 7 = 9$ | $9 - 7 = 2$
$1 + 8 = 9$ | $9 - 8 = 1$
$0 + 9 = 9$ | $9 - 9 = 0$

Number facts for 10

$10 + 0 = 10$ | $10 - 0 = 10$
$9 + 1 = 10$ | $10 - 1 = 9$
$8 + 2 = 10$ | $10 - 2 = 8$
$7 + 3 = 10$ | $10 - 3 = 7$
$6 + 4 = 10$ | $10 - 4 = 6$
$5 + 5 = 10$ | $10 - 5 = 5$
$4 + 6 = 10$ | $10 - 6 = 4$
$3 + 7 = 10$ | $10 - 7 = 3$
$2 + 8 = 10$ | $10 - 8 = 2$
$1 + 9 = 10$ | $10 - 9 = 1$
$0 + 10 = 10$ | $10 - 10 = 0$

Number facts for 11

$11 + 0 = 11$ | $11 - 0 = 11$
$10 + 1 = 11$ | $11 - 1 = 10$
$9 + 2 = 11$ | $11 - 2 = 9$
$8 + 3 = 11$ | $11 - 3 = 8$
$7 + 4 = 11$ | $11 - 4 = 7$
$6 + 5 = 11$ | $11 - 5 = 6$
$5 + 6 = 11$ | $11 - 6 = 5$
$4 + 7 = 11$ | $11 - 7 = 4$
$3 + 8 = 11$ | $11 - 8 = 3$
$2 + 9 = 11$ | $11 - 9 = 2$
$1 + 10 = 11$ | $11 - 10 = 1$
$0 + 11 = 11$ | $11 - 11 = 0$

Number facts for 12

$12 + 0 = 12$ | $12 - 0 = 12$
$11 + 1 = 12$ | $12 - 1 = 11$
$10 + 2 = 12$ | $12 - 2 = 10$
$9 + 3 = 12$ | $12 - 3 = 9$
$8 + 4 = 12$ | $12 - 4 = 8$
$7 + 5 = 12$ | $12 - 5 = 7$
$6 + 6 = 12$ | $12 - 6 = 6$
$5 + 7 = 12$ | $12 - 7 = 5$
$4 + 8 = 12$ | $12 - 8 = 4$
$3 + 9 = 12$ | $12 - 9 = 3$
$2 + 10 = 12$ | $12 - 10 = 2$
$1 + 11 = 12$ | $12 - 11 = 1$
$0 + 12 = 12$ | $12 - 12 = 0$

Number facts for 13

$13 + 0 = 13$ | $13 - 0 = 13$
$12 + 1 = 13$ | $13 - 1 = 12$
$11 + 2 = 13$ | $13 - 2 = 11$
$10 + 3 = 13$ | $13 - 3 = 10$
$9 + 4 = 13$ | $13 - 4 = 9$
$8 + 5 = 13$ | $13 - 5 = 8$
$7 + 6 = 13$ | $13 - 6 = 7$
$6 + 7 = 13$ | $13 - 7 = 6$
$5 + 8 = 13$ | $13 - 8 = 5$
$4 + 9 = 13$ | $13 - 9 = 4$
$3 + 10 = 13$ | $13 - 10 = 3$
$2 + 11 = 13$ | $13 - 11 = 2$
$1 + 12 = 13$ | $13 - 12 = 1$
$0 + 13 = 13$ | $13 - 13 = 0$

Number facts for 14

$14 + 0 = 14$ | $14 - 0 = 14$
$13 + 1 = 14$ | $14 - 1 = 13$
$12 + 2 = 14$ | $14 - 2 = 12$
$11 + 3 = 14$ | $14 - 3 = 11$
$10 + 4 = 14$ | $14 - 4 = 10$
$9 + 5 = 14$ | $14 - 5 = 9$
$8 + 6 = 14$ | $14 - 6 = 8$
$7 + 7 = 14$ | $14 - 7 = 7$
$6 + 8 = 14$ | $14 - 8 = 6$
$5 + 9 = 14$ | $14 - 9 = 5$
$4 + 10 = 14$ | $14 - 10 = 4$
$3 + 11 = 14$ | $14 - 11 = 3$
$2 + 12 = 14$ | $14 - 12 = 2$
$1 + 13 = 14$ | $14 - 13 = 1$
$0 + 14 = 14$ | $14 - 14 = 0$

Fluency in Number Facts

Number facts for 15

15 + 0 = 15	15 − 0 = 15
14 + 1 = 15	15 − 1 = 14
13 + 2 = 15	15 − 2 = 13
12 + 3 = 15	15 − 3 = 12
11 + 4 = 15	15 − 4 = 11
10 + 5 = 15	15 − 5 = 10
9 + 6 = 15	15 − 6 = 9
8 + 7 = 15	15 − 7 = 8
7 + 8 = 15	15 − 8 = 7
6 + 9 = 15	15 − 9 = 6
5 + 10 = 15	15 − 10 = 5
4 + 11 = 15	15 − 11 = 4
3 + 12 = 15	15 − 12 = 3
2 + 13 = 15	15 − 13 = 2
1 + 14 = 15	15 − 14 = 1
0 + 15 = 15	15 − 15 = 0

Number facts for 16

16 + 0 = 16	16 − 0 = 16
15 + 1 = 16	16 − 1 = 15
14 + 2 = 16	16 − 2 = 14
13 + 3 = 16	16 − 3 = 13
12 + 4 = 16	16 − 4 = 12
11 + 5 = 16	16 − 5 = 11
10 + 6 = 16	16 − 6 = 10
9 + 7 = 16	16 − 7 = 9
8 + 8 = 16	16 − 8 = 8
7 + 9 = 16	16 − 9 = 7
6 + 10 = 16	16 − 10 = 6
5 + 11 = 16	16 − 11 = 5
4 + 12 = 16	16 − 12 = 4
3 + 13 = 16	16 − 13 = 3
2 + 14 = 16	16 − 14 = 2
1 + 15 = 16	16 − 15 = 1
0 + 16 = 16	16 − 16 = 0

Number facts for 17

17 + 0 = 17	17 − 0 = 17
16 + 1 = 17	17 − 1 = 16
15 + 2 = 17	17 − 2 = 15
14 + 3 = 17	17 − 3 = 14
13 + 4 = 17	17 − 4 = 13
12 + 5 = 17	17 − 5 = 12
11 + 6 = 17	17 − 6 = 11
10 + 7 = 17	17 − 7 = 10
9 + 8 = 17	17 − 8 = 9
8 + 9 = 17	17 − 9 = 8
7 + 10 = 17	17 − 10 = 7
6 + 11 = 17	17 − 11 = 6
5 + 12 = 17	17 − 12 = 5
4 + 13 = 17	17 − 13 = 4
3 + 14 = 17	17 − 14 = 3
2 + 15 = 17	17 − 15 = 2
1 + 16 = 17	17 − 16 = 1
0 + 17 = 17	17 − 17 = 0

Number facts for 18

18 + 0 = 18	18 − 0 = 18
17 + 1 = 18	18 − 1 = 17
16 + 2 = 18	18 − 2 = 16
15 + 3 = 18	18 − 3 = 15
14 + 4 = 18	18 − 4 = 14
13 + 5 = 18	18 − 5 = 13
12 + 6 = 18	18 − 6 = 12
11 + 7 = 18	18 − 7 = 11
10 + 8 = 18	18 − 8 = 10
9 + 9 = 18	18 − 9 = 9
8 + 10 = 18	18 − 10 = 8
7 + 11 = 18	18 − 11 = 7
6 + 12 = 18	18 − 12 = 6
5 + 13 = 18	18 − 13 = 5
4 + 14 = 18	18 − 14 = 4
3 + 15 = 18	18 − 15 = 3
2 + 16 = 18	18 − 16 = 2
1 + 17 = 18	18 − 17 = 1
0 + 18 = 18	18 − 18 = 0

Number facts for 19

19 + 0 = 19	19 − 0 = 19
18 + 1 = 19	19 − 1 = 18
17 + 2 = 19	19 − 2 = 17
16 + 3 = 19	19 − 3 = 16
15 + 4 = 19	19 − 4 = 15
14 + 5 = 19	19 − 5 = 14
13 + 6 = 19	19 − 6 = 13
12 + 7 = 19	19 − 7 = 12
11 + 8 = 19	19 − 8 = 11
10 + 9 = 19	19 − 9 = 10
9 + 10 = 19	19 − 10 = 9
8 + 11 = 19	19 − 11 = 8
7 + 12 = 19	19 − 12 = 7
6 + 13 = 19	19 − 13 = 6
5 + 14 = 19	19 − 14 = 5
4 + 15 = 19	19 − 15 = 4
3 + 16 = 19	19 − 16 = 3
2 + 17 = 19	19 − 17 = 2
1 + 18 = 19	19 − 18 = 1
0 + 19 = 19	19 − 19 = 0

Number facts for 20

20 + 0 = 20	20 − 0 = 20
19 + 1 = 20	20 − 1 = 19
18 + 2 = 20	20 − 2 = 18
17 + 3 = 20	20 − 3 = 17
16 + 4 = 20	20 − 4 = 16
15 + 5 = 20	20 − 5 = 15
14 + 6 = 20	20 − 6 = 14
13 + 7 = 20	20 − 7 = 13
12 + 8 = 20	20 − 8 = 12
11 + 9 = 20	20 − 9 = 11
10 + 10 = 20	20 − 10 = 10
9 + 11 = 20	20 − 11 = 9
8 + 12 = 20	20 − 12 = 8
7 + 13 = 20	20 − 13 = 7
6 + 14 = 20	20 − 14 = 6
5 + 15 = 20	20 − 15 = 5
4 + 16 = 20	20 − 16 = 4
3 + 17 = 20	20 − 17 = 3
2 + 18 = 20	20 − 18 = 2
1 + 19 = 20	20 − 19 = 1
0 + 20 = 20	20 − 20 = 0

Addition and subtraction trios to 20

Trios for 2

$2 + 0 = 2$
$0 + 2 = 2$
$2 - 0 = 2$
$2 - 2 = 0$

$1 + 1 = 2$
$2 - 1 = 1$

Trios for 3

$3 + 0 = 3$
$0 + 3 = 3$
$3 - 0 = 3$
$3 - 3 = 0$

$2 + 1 = 3$
$1 + 2 = 3$
$3 - 1 = 2$
$3 - 2 = 1$

Trios for 4

$4 + 0 = 4$
$0 + 4 = 4$
$4 - 0 = 4$
$4 - 4 = 0$

$3 + 1 = 4$
$1 + 3 = 4$
$4 - 1 = 3$
$4 - 3 = 1$

$2 + 2 = 4$
$4 - 2 = 2$

Trios for 5

$5 + 0 = 5$
$0 + 5 = 5$
$5 - 0 = 5$
$5 - 5 = 0$

$4 + 1 = 5$
$1 + 4 = 5$
$5 - 1 = 4$
$5 - 4 = 1$

$3 + 2 = 5$
$2 + 3 = 5$
$5 - 2 = 3$
$5 - 3 = 2$

Trios for 6

$6 + 0 = 6$
$0 + 6 = 6$
$6 - 0 = 6$
$6 - 6 = 0$

$5 + 1 = 6$
$1 + 5 = 6$
$6 - 1 = 5$
$6 - 5 = 1$

$4 + 2 = 6$
$2 + 4 = 6$
$6 - 2 = 4$
$6 - 4 = 2$

$3 + 3 = 6$
$6 - 3 = 3$

Trios for 7

7 + 0 = 7
0 + 7 = 7
7 − 0 = 7
7 − 7 = 0

6 + 1 = 7
1 + 6 = 7
7 − 1 = 6
7 − 6 = 1

5 + 2 = 7
2 + 5 = 7
7 − 2 = 5
7 − 5 = 2

4 + 3 = 7
3 + 4 = 7
7 − 3 = 4
7 − 4 = 3

Trios for 8

8 + 0 = 8
0 + 8 = 8
8 − 0 = 8
8 − 8 = 0

7 + 1 = 8
1 + 7 = 8
8 − 1 = 7
8 − 7 = 1

6 + 2 = 8
2 + 6 = 8
8 − 2 = 6
8 − 6 = 2

5 + 3 = 8
3 + 5 = 8
8 − 3 = 5
8 − 5 = 3

4 + 4 = 8
8 − 4 = 4

Trios for 9

9 + 0 = 9
0 + 9 = 9
9 − 0 = 9
9 − 9 = 0

8 + 1 = 9
1 + 8 = 9
9 − 1 = 8
9 − 8 = 1

7 + 2 = 9
2 + 7 = 9
9 − 2 = 7
9 − 7 = 2

6 + 3 = 9
3 + 6 = 9
9 − 3 = 6
9 − 6 = 3

5 + 4 = 9
4 + 5 = 9
9 − 4 = 5
9 − 5 = 4

Trios for 10

10 + 0 = 10
0 + 10 = 10
10 − 0 = 10
10 − 10 = 0

9 + 1 = 10
1 + 9 = 10
10 − 1 = 9
10 − 9 = 1

8 + 2 = 10
2 + 8 = 10
10 − 2 = 8
10 − 8 = 2

7 + 3 = 10
3 + 7 = 10
10 − 3 = 7
10 − 7 = 3

6 + 4 = 10
4 + 6 = 10
10 − 4 = 6
10 − 6 = 4

5 + 5 = 10
10 − 5 = 5

Trios for 11

11 + 0 = 11
0 + 11 = 11
11 − 0 = 11
11 − 11 = 0

10 + 1 = 11
1 + 10 = 11
11 − 1 = 10
11 − 10 = 1

9 + 2 = 11
2 + 9 = 11
11 − 2 = 9
11 − 9 = 2

8 + 3 = 11
3 + 8 = 11
11 − 3 = 8
11 − 8 = 3

7 + 4 = 11
4 + 7 = 11
11 − 4 = 7
11 − 7 = 4

6 + 5 = 11
5 + 6 = 11
11 − 5 = 6
11 − 6 = 5

Trios for 12

12 + 0 = 12
0 + 12 = 12
12 − 0 = 12
12 − 12 = 0

11 + 1 = 12
1 + 11 = 12
12 − 1 = 11
12 − 11 = 1

10 + 2 = 12
2 + 10 = 12
12 − 2 = 10
12 − 10 = 2

9 + 3 = 12
3 + 9 = 12
12 − 3 = 9
12 − 9 = 3

8 + 4 = 12
4 + 8 = 12
12 − 4 = 8
12 − 8 = 4

7 + 5 = 12
5 + 7 = 12
12 − 5 = 7
12 − 7 = 5

6 + 6 = 12
12 − 6 = 6

Trios for 13

13 + 0 = 13
0 + 13 = 13
13 – 0 = 13
13 – 13 = 0

12 + 1 = 13
1 + 12 = 13
13 – 1 = 12
13 – 12 = 1

11 + 2 = 13
2 + 11 = 13
13 – 2 = 11
13 – 11 = 2

10 + 3 = 13
3 + 10 = 13
13 – 3 = 10
13 – 10 = 3

9 + 4 = 13
4 + 9 = 13
13 – 4 = 9
13 – 9 = 4

8 + 5 = 13
5 + 8 = 13
13 – 5 = 8
13 – 8 = 5

7 + 6 = 13
6 + 7 = 13
13 – 6 = 7
13 – 7 = 6

Trios for 14

14 + 0 = 14
0 + 14 = 14
14 – 0 = 14
14 – 14 = 0

13 + 1 = 14
1 + 13 = 14
14 – 1 = 13
14 – 13 = 1

12 + 2 = 14
2 + 12 = 14
14 – 2 = 12
14 – 12 = 2

11 + 3 = 14
3 + 11 = 14
14 – 3 = 11
14 – 11 = 3

10 + 4 = 14
4 + 10 = 14
14 – 4 = 10
14 – 10 = 4

9 + 5 = 14
5 + 9 = 14
14 – 5 = 9
14 – 9 = 5

8 + 6 = 14
6 + 8 = 14
14 – 6 = 8
14 – 8 = 6

7 + 7 = 14
14 – 7 = 7

Trios for 15

15 + 0 = 15
0 + 15 = 15
15 − 0 = 15
15 − 15 = 0

14 + 1 = 15
1 + 14 = 15
15 − 1 = 14
15 − 14 = 1

13 + 2 = 15
2 + 13 = 15
15 − 2 = 13
15 − 13 = 2

12 + 3 = 15
3 + 12 = 15
15 − 3 = 12
15 − 12 = 3

11 + 4 = 15
4 + 11 = 15
15 − 4 = 11
15 − 11 = 4

10 + 5 = 15
5 + 10 = 15
15 − 5 = 10
15 − 10 = 5

9 + 6 = 15
6 + 9 = 15
15 − 6 = 9
15 − 9 = 6

8 + 7 = 15
7 + 8 = 15
15 − 7 = 8
15 − 8 = 7

Trios for 16

16 + 0 = 16
0 + 16 = 16
16 − 0 = 16
16 − 16 = 0

15 + 1 = 16
1 + 15 = 16
16 − 1 = 15
16 − 15 = 1

14 + 2 = 16
2 + 14 = 16
16 − 2 = 14
16 − 14 = 2

13 + 3 = 16
3 + 13 = 16
16 − 3 = 13
16 − 13 = 3

12 + 4 = 16
4 + 12 = 16
16 − 4 = 12
16 − 12 = 4

11 + 5 = 16
5 + 11 = 16
16 − 5 = 11
16 − 11 = 5

10 + 6 = 16
6 + 10 = 16
16 − 6 = 10
16 − 10 = 6

9 + 7 = 16
7 + 9 = 16
16 − 7 = 9
16 − 9 = 7

8 + 8 = 16
16 − 8 = 8

Trios for 17

17 + 0 = 17
0 + 17 = 17
17 − 0 = 17
17 − 17 = 0

16 + 1 = 17
1 + 16 = 17
17 − 1 = 16
17 − 16 = 1

15 + 2 = 17
2 + 15 = 17
17 − 2 = 15
17 − 15 = 2

14 + 3 = 17
3 + 14 = 17
17 − 3 = 14
17 − 14 = 3

13 + 4 = 17
4 + 13 = 17
17 − 4 = 13
17 − 13 = 4

12 + 5 = 17
5 + 12 = 17
17 − 5 = 12
17 − 12 = 5

11 + 6 = 17
6 + 11 = 17
17 − 6 = 11
17 − 11 = 6

10 + 7 = 17
7 + 10 = 17
17 − 7 = 10
17 − 10 = 7

9 + 8 = 17
8 + 9 = 17
17 − 8 = 9
17 − 9 = 8

Trios for 18

18 + 0 = 18
0 + 18 = 18
18 − 0 = 18
18 − 18 = 0

17 + 1 = 18
1 + 17 = 18
18 − 1 = 17
18 − 17 = 1

16 + 2 = 18
2 + 16 = 18
18 − 2 = 16
18 − 16 = 2

15 + 3 = 18
3 + 15 = 18
18 − 3 = 15
18 − 15 = 3

14 + 4 = 18
4 + 14 = 18
18 − 4 = 14
18 − 14 = 4

13 + 5 = 18
5 + 13 = 18
18 − 5 = 13
18 − 13 = 5

12 + 6 = 18
6 + 12 = 18
18 − 6 = 12
18 − 12 = 6

11 + 7 = 18
7 + 11 = 18
18 − 7 = 11
18 − 11 = 7

10 + 8 = 18
8 + 10 = 18
18 − 8 = 10
18 − 10 = 8

9 + 9 = 18
18 − 9 = 9

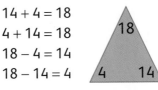
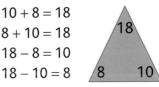

Maths facts – Addition and subtraction

Trios for 19

19 + 0 = 19
0 + 19 = 19
19 − 0 = 19
19 − 19 = 0

18 + 1 = 19
1 + 18 = 19
19 − 1 = 18
19 − 18 = 1

17 + 2 = 19
2 + 17 = 19
19 − 2 = 17
19 − 17 = 2
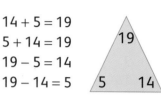

16 + 3 = 19
3 + 16 = 19
19 − 3 = 16
19 − 16 = 3

15 + 4 = 19
4 + 15 = 19
19 − 4 = 15
19 − 15 = 4

14 + 5 = 19
5 + 14 = 19
19 − 5 = 14
19 − 14 = 5
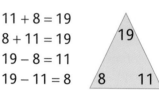

13 + 6 = 19
6 + 13 = 19
19 − 6 = 13
19 − 13 = 6

12 + 7 = 19
7 + 12 = 19
19 − 7 = 12
19 − 12 = 7

11 + 8 = 19
8 + 11 = 19
19 − 8 = 11
19 − 11 = 8

10 + 9 = 19
9 + 10 = 19
19 − 9 = 10
19 − 10 = 9

Trios for 20

20 + 0 = 20
0 + 20 = 20
20 − 0 = 20
20 − 20 = 0

19 + 1 = 20
1 + 19 = 20
20 − 1 = 19
20 − 19 = 1

18 + 2 = 20
2 + 18 = 20
20 − 2 = 18
20 − 18 = 2

17 + 3 = 20
3 + 17 = 20
20 − 3 = 17
20 − 17 = 3

16 + 4 = 20
4 + 16 = 20
20 − 4 = 16
20 − 16 = 4

15 + 5 = 20
5 + 15 = 20
20 − 5 = 15
20 − 15 = 5

14 + 6 = 20
6 + 14 = 20
20 − 6 = 14
20 − 14 = 6

13 + 7 = 20
7 + 13 = 20
20 − 7 = 13
20 − 13 = 7
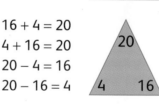

12 + 8 = 20
8 + 12 = 20
20 − 8 = 12
20 − 12 = 8
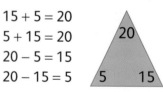

11 + 9 = 20
9 + 11 = 20
20 − 9 = 11
20 − 11 = 9
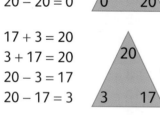

10 + 10 = 20
20 − 10 = 10
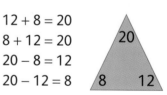

Fluency in Number Facts

Addition number facts to 10 and 20 table

Addition can be done in any order.

So, 2 + 3 = 5 and 3 + 2 = 5

Addition is the opposite of subtraction.

So, if you know that 3 + 2 = 5 you also know that:

5 − 3 = 2 and 5 − 2 = 3

+	0	1	2	3	4	5	6	7	8	9	10
0	0	1	2	3	4	5	6	7	8	9	10
1	1	2	3	4	5	6	7	8	9	10	11
2	2	3	4	5	6	7	8	9	10	11	12
3	3	4	5	6	7	8	9	10	11	12	13
4	4	5	6	7	8	9	10	11	12	13	14
5	5	6	7	8	9	10	11	12	13	14	15
6	6	7	8	9	10	11	12	13	14	15	16
7	7	8	9	10	11	12	13	14	15	16	17
8	8	9	10	11	12	13	14	15	16	17	18
9	9	10	11	12	13	14	15	16	17	18	19
10	10	11	12	13	14	15	16	17	18	19	20

Addition of 1-digit and 2-digit numbers to 20 table

+	11	12	13	14	15	16	17	18	19	20
0	11	12	13	14	15	16	17	18	19	20
1	12	13	14	15	16	17	18	19	20	
2	13	14	15	16	17	18	19	20		
3	14	15	16	17	18	19	20			
4	15	16	17	18	19	20				
5	16	17	18	19	20					
6	17	18	19	20						
7	18	19	20							
8	19	20								
9	20									

Multiples of 10 addition and subtraction table

If you know that
$6 + 8 = 14$, then you can
use this to work out facts
such as:

$60 + 80 = 140$

$600 + 800 = 1400$

Addition can be done
in any order.

So, $60 + 80 = 140$

and $80 + 60 = 140$

Addition is the inverse
of subtraction. So,
if you know that
$60 + 80 = 140$
you also know that:

$140 - 60 = 80$

$140 - 80 = 60$

+	0	10	20	30	40	50	60	70	80	90	100
0	0	10	20	30	40	50	60	70	80	90	100
10	10	20	30	40	50	60	70	80	90	100	110
20	20	30	40	50	60	70	80	90	100	110	120
30	30	40	50	60	70	80	90	100	110	120	130
40	40	50	60	70	80	90	100	110	120	130	140
50	50	60	70	80	90	100	110	120	130	140	150
60	60	70	80	90	100	110	120	130	140	150	160
70	70	80	90	100	110	120	130	140	150	160	170
80	80	90	100	110	120	130	140	150	160	170	180
90	90	100	110	120	130	140	150	160	170	180	190
100	100	110	120	130	140	150	160	170	180	190	200

If you know that 14 + 3 = 17, then you can use this to work out facts such as:

140 + 30 = 170

Addition can be done in any order.

So, 140 + 30 = 170

and 30 + 140 = 170

Addition is the inverse of subtraction. So, if you know that 140 + 30 = 170 you also know that:

170 − 30 = 140

170 − 140 = 30

+	110	120	130	140	150	160	170	180	190	200
0	110	120	130	140	150	160	170	180	190	200
10	120	130	140	150	160	170	180	190	200	210
20	130	140	150	160	170	180	190	200	210	220
30	140	150	160	170	180	190	200	210	220	230
40	150	160	170	180	190	200	210	220	230	240
50	160	170	180	190	200	210	220	230	240	250
60	170	180	190	200	210	220	230	240	250	260
70	180	190	200	210	220	230	240	250	260	270
80	190	200	210	220	230	240	250	260	270	280
90	200	210	220	230	240	250	260	270	280	290
100	210	220	230	240	250	260	270	280	290	300

Decimals addition and subtraction table

If you know that 2 + 5 = 7, then you can also work out facts such as:

0·2 + 0·5 = 0·7

Addition can be done in any order.

So, 0·2 + 0·5 = 0·7

and 0·5 + 0·2 = 0·7

Addition is the inverse of subtraction. So, if you know that 0·2 + 0·5 = 0·7 you also know that:

0·7 − 0·2 = 0·5

0·7 − 0·5 = 0·2

+	0	0.1	0.2	0.3	0.4	0.5	0.6	0.7	0.8	0.9	1
0	0	0.1	0.2	0.3	0.4	0.5	0.6	0.7	0.8	0.9	1
0.1	0.1	0.2	0.3	0.4	0.5	0.6	0.7	0.8	0.9	1	1.1
0.2	0.2	0.3	0.4	0.5	0.6	0.7	0.8	0.9	1	1.1	1.2
0.3	0.3	0.4	0.5	0.6	0.7	0.8	0.9	1	1.1	1.2	1.3
0.4	0.4	0.5	0.6	0.7	1.8	0.9	1	1.1	1.2	1.3	1.4
0.5	0.5	0.6	0.7	0.8	0.9	1	1.1	1.2	1.3	1.4	1.5
0.6	0.6	0.7	0.8	0.9	1	1.1	1.2	1.3	1.4	1.5	1.6
0.7	0.7	0.8	0.9	1	1.1	1.2	1.3	1.4	1.5	1.6	1.7
0.8	0.8	0.9	1	1.1	1.2	1.3	1.4	1.5	1.6	1.7	1.8
0.9	0.9	1	1.1	1.2	1.3	1.4	1.5	1.6	1.7	1.8	1.9
1	1	1.1	1.2	1.3	1.4	1.5	1.6	1.7	1.8	1.9	2

If you know that $2 + 5 = 7$, then you can also work out facts such as:

$0.02 + 0.05 = 0.07$

Addition can be done in any order.

So, $0.02 + 0.05 = 0.07$

and $0.05 + 0.02 = 0.07$

Addition is the inverse of subtraction. So, if you know that $0.02 + 0.05 = 0.07$ you also know that:

$0.07 - 0.02 = 0.05$

$0.07 - 0.05 = 0.02$

+	0	0.01	0.02	0.03	0.04	0.05	0.06	0.07	0.08	0.09	0.1
0	0	0.01	0.02	0.03	0.04	0.05	0.06	0.07	0.08	0.09	0.1
0.01	0.01	0.02	0.03	0.04	0.05	0.06	0.07	0.08	0.09	0.1	0.11
0.02	0.02	0.03	0.04	0.05	0.06	0.07	0.08	0.09	0.1	0.11	0.12
0.03	0.03	0.04	0.05	0.06	0.07	0.08	0.09	0.1	0.11	0.12	0.13
0.04	0.04	0.05	0.06	0.07	0.08	0.09	0.1	0.11	0.12	0.13	0.14
0.05	0.05	0.06	0.07	0.08	0.09	0.1	0.11	0.12	0.13	0.14	0.15
0.06	0.06	0.07	0.08	0.09	0.1	0.11	0.12	0.13	0.14	0.15	0.16
0.07	0.07	0.08	0.09	0.1	0.11	0.12	0.13	0.14	0.15	0.16	0.17
0.08	0.08	0.09	0.1	0.11	0.12	0.13	0.14	0.15	0.16	0.17	0.18
0.09	0.09	0.1	0.11	0.12	0.13	0.14	0.15	0.16	0.17	0.18	0.19
0.1	0.1	0.11	0.12	0.13	0.14	0.15	0.16	0.17	0.18	0.19	0.2

Multiplication tables to 12 × 12 and involving multiples of 10

2 times table

 1 × 2 = 2
 2 × 2 = 4
3 × 2 = 6
4 × 2 = 8
 5 × 2 = 10
6 × 2 = 12
7 × 2 = 14
8 × 2 = 16
9 × 2 = 18
 10 × 2 = 20
11 × 2 = 22
12 × 2 = 24

4 times table

 1 × 4 = 4
 2 × 4 = 8
3 × 4 = 12
4 × 4 = 16
 5 × 4 = 20
6 × 4 = 24
7 × 4 = 28
8 × 4 = 32
9 × 4 = 36
 10 × 4 = 40
11 × 4 = 44
12 × 4 = 48

8 times table

1 × 8 = 8
2 × 8 = 16
3 × 8 = 24
4 × 8 = 32
5 × 8 = 40
6 × 8 = 48
7 × 8 = 56
8 × 8 = 64
9 × 8 = 72
10 × 8 = 80
11 × 8 = 88
12 × 8 = 96

---

1 × 20 = 20
2 × 20 = 40
3 × 20 = 60
4 × 20 = 80
5 × 20 = 100
6 × 20 = 120
7 × 20 = 140
8 × 20 = 160
9 × 20 = 180
10 × 20 = 200
11 × 20 = 220
12 × 20 = 240

1 × 40 = 40
2 × 40 = 80
3 × 40 = 120
4 × 40 = 160
5 × 40 = 200
6 × 40 = 240
7 × 40 = 280
8 × 40 = 320
9 × 40 = 360
10 × 40 = 400
11 × 40 = 440
12 × 40 = 480

1 × 80 = 80
2 × 80 = 160
3 × 80 = 240
4 × 80 = 320
5 × 80 = 400
6 × 80 = 480
7 × 80 = 560
8 × 80 = 640
9 × 80 = 720
10 × 80 = 800
11 × 80 = 880
12 × 80 = 960

3 times table

 $1 \times 3 = 3$
$2 \times 3 = 6$
$3 \times 3 = 9$
$4 \times 3 = 12$
$5 \times 3 = 15$
$6 \times 3 = 18$
$7 \times 3 = 21$
$8 \times 3 = 24$
$9 \times 3 = 27$
$10 \times 3 = 30$
$11 \times 3 = 33$
$12 \times 3 = 36$

6 times table

$1 \times 6 = 6$
$2 \times 6 = 12$
$3 \times 6 = 18$
$4 \times 6 = 24$
$5 \times 6 = 30$
$6 \times 6 = 36$
$7 \times 6 = 42$
$8 \times 6 = 48$
$9 \times 6 = 54$
$10 \times 6 = 60$
$11 \times 6 = 66$
$12 \times 6 = 72$

12 times table

$1 \times 12 = 12$
$2 \times 12 = 24$
$3 \times 12 = 36$
$4 \times 12 = 48$
$5 \times 12 = 60$
$6 \times 12 = 72$
$7 \times 12 = 84$
$8 \times 12 = 96$
$9 \times 12 = 108$
$10 \times 12 = 120$
$11 \times 12 = 132$
$12 \times 12 = 144$

$1 \times 30 = 30$
$2 \times 30 = 60$
$3 \times 30 = 90$
$4 \times 30 = 120$
$5 \times 30 = 150$
$6 \times 30 = 180$
$7 \times 30 = 210$
$8 \times 30 = 240$
$9 \times 30 = 270$
$10 \times 30 = 300$
$11 \times 30 = 330$
$12 \times 30 = 360$

$1 \times 60 = 60$
$2 \times 60 = 120$
$3 \times 60 = 180$
$4 \times 60 = 240$
$5 \times 60 = 300$
$6 \times 60 = 360$
$7 \times 60 = 420$
$8 \times 60 = 480$
$9 \times 60 = 540$
$10 \times 60 = 600$
$11 \times 60 = 660$
$12 \times 60 = 720$

$1 \times 120 = 120$
$2 \times 120 = 240$
$3 \times 120 = 360$
$4 \times 120 = 480$
$5 \times 120 = 600$
$6 \times 120 = 720$
$7 \times 120 = 840$
$8 \times 120 = 960$
$9 \times 120 = 1080$
$10 \times 120 = 1200$
$11 \times 120 = 1320$
$12 \times 120 = 1440$

5 times table

1 × 5 = 5
2 × 5 = 10
3 × 5 = 15
4 × 5 = 20
5 × 5 = 25
6 × 5 = 30
7 × 5 = 35
8 × 5 = 40
9 × 5 = 45
10 × 5 = 50
11 × 5 = 55
12 × 5 = 60

10 times table

1 × 10 = 10
2 × 10 = 20
3 × 10 = 30
4 × 10 = 40
5 × 10 = 50
6 × 10 = 60
7 × 10 = 70
8 × 10 = 80
9 × 10 = 90
10 × 10 = 100
11 × 10 = 110
12 × 10 = 120

1 × 50 = 50
2 × 50 = 100
3 × 50 = 150
4 × 50 = 200
5 × 50 = 250
6 × 50 = 300
7 × 50 = 350
8 × 50 = 400
9 × 50 = 450
10 × 50 = 500
11 × 50 = 550
12 × 50 = 600

1 × 100 = 100
2 × 100 = 200
3 × 100 = 300
4 × 100 = 400
5 × 100 = 500
6 × 100 = 600
7 × 100 = 700
8 × 100 = 800
9 × 100 = 900
10 × 100 = 1000
11 × 100 = 1100
12 × 100 = 1200

7 times table

$1 \times 7 = 7$
$2 \times 7 = 14$
$3 \times 7 = 21$
$4 \times 7 = 28$
$5 \times 7 = 35$
$6 \times 7 = 42$
$7 \times 7 = 49$
$8 \times 7 = 56$
$9 \times 7 = 63$
$10 \times 7 = 70$
$11 \times 7 = 77$
$12 \times 7 = 84$

9 times table

$1 \times 9 = 9$
$2 \times 9 = 18$
$3 \times 9 = 27$
$4 \times 9 = 36$
$5 \times 9 = 45$
$6 \times 9 = 54$
$7 \times 9 = 63$
$8 \times 9 = 72$
$9 \times 9 = 81$
$10 \times 9 = 90$
$11 \times 9 = 99$
$12 \times 9 = 108$

11 times table

$1 \times 11 = 11$
$2 \times 11 = 22$
$3 \times 11 = 33$
$4 \times 11 = 44$
$5 \times 11 = 55$
$6 \times 11 = 66$
$7 \times 11 = 77$
$8 \times 11 = 88$
$9 \times 11 = 99$
$10 \times 11 = 110$
$11 \times 11 = 121$
$12 \times 11 = 132$

$1 \times 70 = 70$
$2 \times 70 = 140$
$3 \times 70 = 210$
$4 \times 70 = 280$
$5 \times 70 = 350$
$6 \times 70 = 420$
$7 \times 70 = 490$
$8 \times 70 = 560$
$9 \times 70 = 630$
$10 \times 70 = 700$
$11 \times 70 = 770$
$12 \times 70 = 840$

$1 \times 90 = 90$
$2 \times 90 = 180$
$3 \times 90 = 270$
$4 \times 90 = 360$
$5 \times 90 = 450$
$6 \times 90 = 540$
$7 \times 90 = 630$
$8 \times 90 = 720$
$9 \times 90 = 810$
$10 \times 90 = 900$
$11 \times 90 = 990$
$12 \times 90 = 1080$

$1 \times 110 = 110$
$2 \times 110 = 220$
$3 \times 110 = 330$
$4 \times 110 = 440$
$5 \times 110 = 550$
$6 \times 110 = 660$
$7 \times 110 = 770$
$8 \times 110 = 880$
$9 \times 110 = 990$
$10 \times 110 = 1100$
$11 \times 110 = 1210$
$12 \times 110 = 1320$

Division facts relating to the multiplication tables to 12 × 12 and involving multiples of 10

Division facts related to the 2 times table

$2 \div 2 = 1$
$4 \div 2 = 2$
$6 \div 2 = 3$
$8 \div 2 = 4$
$10 \div 2 = 5$
$12 \div 2 = 6$
$14 \div 2 = 7$
$16 \div 2 = 8$
$18 \div 2 = 9$
$20 \div 2 = 10$
$22 \div 2 = 11$
$24 \div 2 = 12$

Division facts related to the 4 times table

$4 \div 4 = 1$
$8 \div 4 = 2$
$12 \div 4 = 3$
$16 \div 4 = 4$
$20 \div 4 = 5$
$24 \div 4 = 6$
$28 \div 4 = 7$
$32 \div 4 = 8$
$36 \div 4 = 9$
$40 \div 4 = 10$
$44 \div 4 = 11$
$48 \div 4 = 12$

Division facts related to the 8 times table

$8 \div 8 = 1$
$16 \div 8 = 2$
$24 \div 8 = 3$
$32 \div 8 = 4$
$40 \div 8 = 5$
$48 \div 8 = 6$
$56 \div 8 = 7$
$64 \div 8 = 8$
$72 \div 8 = 9$
$80 \div 8 = 10$
$88 \div 8 = 11$
$96 \div 8 = 12$

$20 \div 20 = 1$
$40 \div 20 = 2$
$60 \div 20 = 3$
$80 \div 20 = 4$
$100 \div 20 = 5$
$120 \div 20 = 6$
$140 \div 20 = 7$
$160 \div 20 = 8$
$180 \div 20 = 9$
$200 \div 20 = 10$
$220 \div 20 = 11$
$240 \div 20 = 12$

$40 \div 40 = 1$
$80 \div 40 = 2$
$120 \div 40 = 3$
$160 \div 40 = 4$
$200 \div 40 = 5$
$240 \div 40 = 6$
$280 \div 40 = 7$
$320 \div 40 = 8$
$360 \div 40 = 9$
$400 \div 40 = 10$
$440 \div 40 = 11$
$480 \div 40 = 12$

$80 \div 80 = 1$
$160 \div 80 = 2$
$240 \div 80 = 3$
$320 \div 80 = 4$
$400 \div 80 = 5$
$480 \div 80 = 6$
$560 \div 80 = 7$
$640 \div 80 = 8$
$720 \div 80 = 9$
$800 \div 80 = 10$
$880 \div 80 = 11$
$960 \div 80 = 12$

Division facts related to the 3 times table

$3 \div 3 = 1$
$6 \div 3 = 2$
$9 \div 3 = 3$
$12 \div 3 = 4$
$15 \div 3 = 5$
$18 \div 3 = 6$
$21 \div 3 = 7$
$24 \div 3 = 8$
$27 \div 3 = 9$
$30 \div 3 = 10$
$33 \div 3 = 11$
$36 \div 3 = 12$

Division facts related to the 6 times table

$6 \div 6 = 1$
$12 \div 6 = 2$
$18 \div 6 = 3$
$24 \div 6 = 4$
$30 \div 6 = 5$
$36 \div 6 = 6$
$42 \div 6 = 7$
$48 \div 6 = 8$
$54 \div 6 = 9$
$60 \div 6 = 10$
$66 \div 6 = 11$
$72 \div 6 = 12$

Division facts related to the 12 times table

$12 \div 12 = 1$
$24 \div 12 = 2$
$36 \div 12 = 3$
$48 \div 12 = 4$
$60 \div 12 = 5$
$72 \div 12 = 6$
$84 \div 12 = 7$
$96 \div 12 = 8$
$108 \div 12 = 9$
$120 \div 12 = 10$
$132 \div 12 = 11$
$144 \div 12 = 12$

$30 \div 30 = 1$
$60 \div 30 = 2$
$90 \div 30 = 3$
$120 \div 30 = 4$
$150 \div 30 = 5$
$180 \div 30 = 6$
$210 \div 30 = 7$
$240 \div 30 = 8$
$270 \div 30 = 9$
$300 \div 30 = 10$
$330 \div 30 = 11$
$360 \div 30 = 12$

$60 \div 60 = 1$
$120 \div 60 = 2$
$180 \div 60 = 3$
$240 \div 60 = 4$
$300 \div 60 = 5$
$360 \div 60 = 6$
$420 \div 60 = 7$
$480 \div 60 = 8$
$540 \div 60 = 9$
$600 \div 60 = 10$
$660 \div 60 = 11$
$720 \div 60 = 12$

$120 \div 120 = 1$
$240 \div 120 = 2$
$360 \div 120 = 3$
$480 \div 120 = 4$
$600 \div 120 = 5$
$720 \div 120 = 6$
$840 \div 120 = 7$
$960 \div 120 = 8$
$1080 \div 120 = 9$
$1200 \div 120 = 10$
$1320 \div 120 = 11$
$1440 \div 120 = 12$

Division facts related to the 5 times table

$5 \div 5 = 1$
$10 \div 5 = 2$
$15 \div 5 = 3$
$20 \div 5 = 4$
$25 \div 5 = 5$
$30 \div 5 = 6$
$35 \div 5 = 7$
$40 \div 5 = 8$
$45 \div 5 = 9$
$50 \div 5 = 10$
$55 \div 5 = 11$
$60 \div 5 = 12$

Division facts related to the 10 times table

$10 \div 10 = 1$
$20 \div 10 = 2$
$30 \div 10 = 3$
$40 \div 10 = 4$
$50 \div 10 = 5$
$60 \div 10 = 6$
$70 \div 10 = 7$
$80 \div 10 = 8$
$90 \div 10 = 9$
$100 \div 10 = 10$
$110 \div 10 = 11$
$120 \div 10 = 12$

$50 \div 50 = 1$
$100 \div 50 = 2$
$150 \div 50 = 3$
$200 \div 50 = 4$
$250 \div 50 = 5$
$300 \div 50 = 6$
$350 \div 50 = 7$
$400 \div 50 = 8$
$450 \div 50 = 9$
$500 \div 50 = 10$
$550 \div 50 = 11$
$600 \div 50 = 12$

$100 \div 100 = 1$
$200 \div 100 = 2$
$300 \div 100 = 3$
$400 \div 100 = 4$
$500 \div 100 = 5$
$600 \div 100 = 6$
$700 \div 100 = 7$
$800 \div 100 = 8$
$900 \div 100 = 9$
$1000 \div 100 = 10$
$1100 \div 100 = 11$
$1200 \div 100 = 12$

Division facts related to the 7 times table

$7 \div 7 = 1$
$14 \div 7 = 2$
$21 \div 7 = 3$
$28 \div 7 = 4$
$35 \div 7 = 5$
$42 \div 7 = 6$
$49 \div 7 = 7$
$56 \div 7 = 8$
$63 \div 7 = 9$
$70 \div 7 = 10$
$77 \div 7 = 11$
$84 \div 7 = 12$

Division facts related to the 9 times table

$9 \div 9 = 1$
$18 \div 9 = 2$
$27 \div 9 = 3$
$36 \div 9 = 4$
$45 \div 9 = 5$
$54 \div 9 = 6$
$63 \div 9 = 7$
$72 \div 9 = 8$
$81 \div 9 = 9$
$90 \div 9 = 10$
$99 \div 9 = 11$
$108 \div 9 = 12$

Division facts related to the 11 times table

$11 \div 11 = 1$
$22 \div 11 = 2$
$33 \div 11 = 3$
$44 \div 11 = 4$
$55 \div 11 = 5$
$66 \div 11 = 6$
$77 \div 11 = 7$
$88 \div 11 = 8$
$99 \div 11 = 9$
$110 \div 11 = 10$
$121 \div 11 = 11$
$132 \div 11 = 12$

$70 \div 70 = 1$
$140 \div 70 = 2$
$210 \div 70 = 3$
$280 \div 70 = 4$
$350 \div 70 = 5$
$420 \div 70 = 6$
$490 \div 70 = 7$
$560 \div 70 = 8$
$630 \div 70 = 9$
$700 \div 70 = 10$
$770 \div 70 = 11$
$840 \div 70 = 12$

$90 \div 90 = 1$
$180 \div 90 = 2$
$270 \div 90 = 3$
$360 \div 90 = 4$
$450 \div 90 = 5$
$540 \div 90 = 6$
$630 \div 90 = 7$
$720 \div 90 = 8$
$810 \div 90 = 9$
$900 \div 90 = 10$
$990 \div 90 = 11$
$1080 \div 90 = 12$

$110 \div 110 = 1$
$220 \div 110 = 2$
$330 \div 110 = 3$
$440 \div 110 = 4$
$550 \div 110 = 5$
$660 \div 110 = 6$
$770 \div 110 = 7$
$880 \div 110 = 8$
$990 \div 110 = 9$
$1100 \div 110 = 10$
$1210 \div 110 = 11$
$1320 \div 110 = 12$

Multiples up to 12 × 12

Multiples of 2

1	2	3	4	5	6	7	8	9	10	11	12

| 2 | 4 | 6 | 8 | 10 | 12 | 14 | 16 | 18 | 20 | 22 | 24 |

Multiples of 4

1	2	3	4	5	6	7	8	9	10	11	12

| 4 | 8 | 12 | 16 | 20 | 24 | 28 | 32 | 36 | 40 | 44 | 48 |

Multiples of 8

1	2	3	4	5	6	7	8	9	10	11	12

| 8 | 16 | 24 | 32 | 40 | 48 | 56 | 64 | 72 | 80 | 88 | 96 |

Multiples of 3

1	2	3	4	5	6	7	8	9	10	11	12

| 3 | 6 | 9 | 12 | 15 | 18 | 21 | 24 | 27 | 30 | 33 | 36 |

Multiples of 6

1	2	3	4	5	6	7	8	9	10	11	12

| 6 | 12 | 18 | 24 | 30 | 36 | 42 | 48 | 54 | 60 | 66 | 72 |

Multiples of 12

1	2	3	4	5	6	7	8	9	10	11	12

| 12 | 24 | 36 | 48 | 60 | 72 | 84 | 96 | 108 | 120 | 132 | 144 |

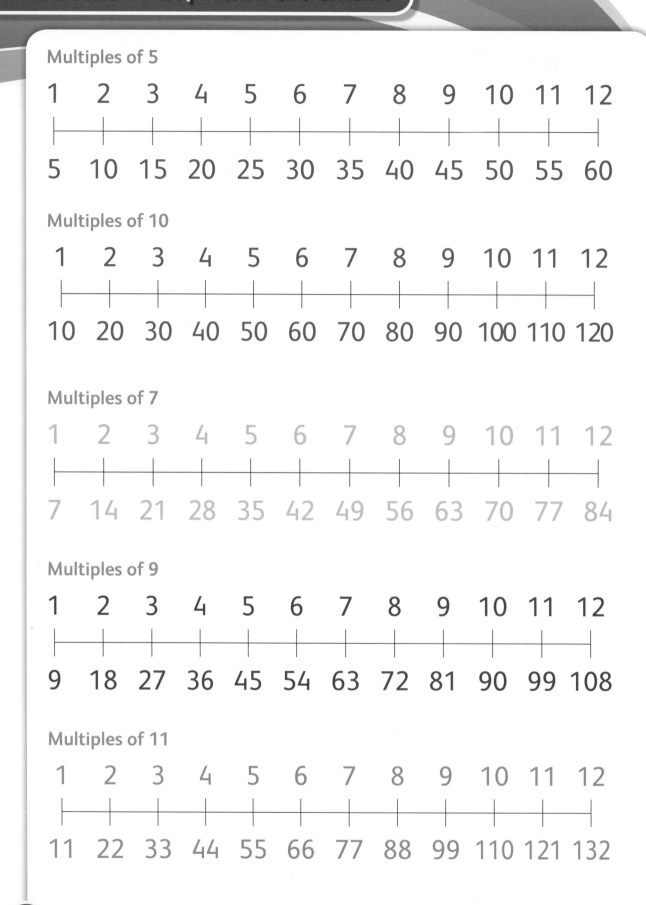

Multiples of 5

| 1 | 2 | 3 | 4 | 5 | 6 | 7 | 8 | 9 | 10 | 11 | 12 |
| 5 | 10 | 15 | 20 | 25 | 30 | 35 | 40 | 45 | 50 | 55 | 60 |

Multiples of 10

| 1 | 2 | 3 | 4 | 5 | 6 | 7 | 8 | 9 | 10 | 11 | 12 |
| 10 | 20 | 30 | 40 | 50 | 60 | 70 | 80 | 90 | 100 | 110 | 120 |

Multiples of 7

| 1 | 2 | 3 | 4 | 5 | 6 | 7 | 8 | 9 | 10 | 11 | 12 |
| 7 | 14 | 21 | 28 | 35 | 42 | 49 | 56 | 63 | 70 | 77 | 84 |

Multiples of 9

| 1 | 2 | 3 | 4 | 5 | 6 | 7 | 8 | 9 | 10 | 11 | 12 |
| 9 | 18 | 27 | 36 | 45 | 54 | 63 | 72 | 81 | 90 | 99 | 108 |

Multiples of 11

| 1 | 2 | 3 | 4 | 5 | 6 | 7 | 8 | 9 | 10 | 11 | 12 |
| 11 | 22 | 33 | 44 | 55 | 66 | 77 | 88 | 99 | 110 | 121 | 132 |

Multiplication square to 12 × 12

×	2	3	4	5	6	7	8	9	10	11	12
1	1×2	1×3	1×4	1×5	1×6	1×7	1×8	1×9	1×10	1×11	1×12
2	2×2	2×3	2×4	2×5	2×6	2×7	2×8	2×9	2×10	2×11	2×12
3	3×2	3×3	3×4	3×5	3×6	3×7	3×8	3×9	3×10	3×11	3×12
4	4×2	4×3	4×4	4×5	4×6	4×7	4×8	4×9	4×10	4×11	4×12
5	5×2	5×3	5×4	5×5	5×6	5×7	5×8	5×9	5×10	5×11	5×12
6	6×2	6×3	6×4	6×5	6×6	6×7	6×8	6×9	6×10	6×11	6×12
7	7×2	7×3	7×4	7×5	7×6	7×7	7×8	7×9	7×10	7×11	7×12
8	8×2	8×3	8×4	8×5	8×6	8×7	8×8	8×9	8×10	8×11	8×12
9	9×2	9×3	9×4	9×5	9×6	9×7	9×8	9×9	9×10	9×11	9×12
10	10×2	10×3	10×4	10×5	10×6	10×7	10×8	10×9	10×10	10×11	10×12
11	11×2	11×3	11×4	11×5	11×6	11×7	11×8	11×9	11×10	11×11	11×12
12	12×2	12×3	12×4	12×5	12×6	12×7	12×8	12×9	12×10	12×11	12×12

×	2	3	4	5	6	7	8	9	10	11	12
1	2	3	4	5	6	7	8	9	10	11	12
2	4	6	8	10	12	14	16	18	20	22	24
3	6	9	12	15	18	21	24	27	30	33	36
4	8	12	16	20	24	28	32	36	40	44	48
5	10	15	20	25	30	35	40	45	50	55	60
6	12	18	24	30	36	42	48	54	60	66	72
7	14	21	28	35	42	49	56	63	70	77	84
8	16	24	32	40	48	56	64	72	80	88	96
9	18	27	36	45	54	63	72	81	90	99	108
10	20	30	40	50	60	70	80	90	100	110	120
11	22	33	44	55	66	77	88	99	110	121	132
12	24	36	48	60	72	84	96	108	120	132	144

Multiples of 10 multiplication square

×	20	30	40	50	60	70	80	90	100	110	120
1	20	30	40	50	60	70	80	90	100	110	120
2	40	60	80	100	120	140	160	180	200	220	240
3	60	90	120	150	180	210	240	270	300	330	360
4	80	120	160	200	240	280	320	360	400	440	480
5	100	150	200	250	300	350	400	450	500	550	600
6	120	180	240	300	360	420	480	540	600	660	720
7	140	210	280	350	420	490	560	630	700	770	840
8	160	240	320	400	480	560	640	720	800	880	960
9	180	270	360	450	540	630	720	810	900	990	1080
10	200	300	400	500	600	700	800	900	1000	1100	1200
11	220	330	440	550	660	770	880	990	1100	1210	1320
12	240	360	480	600	720	840	960	1080	1200	1320	1440

Decimals multiplication square

×	0·2	0·3	0·4	0·5	0·6	0·7	0·8	0·9	1	1·1	1·2
1	0·2	0·3	0·4	0·5	0·6	0·7	0·8	0·9	1	1·1	1·2
2	0·4	0·6	0·8	1	1·2	1·4	1·6	1·8	2	2·2	2·4
3	0·6	0·9	1·2	1·5	1·8	2·1	2·4	2·7	3	3·3	3·6
4	0·8	1·2	1·6	2	2·4	2·8	3·2	3·6	4	4·4	4·8
5	1	1·5	2	2·5	3	3·5	4	4·5	5	5·5	6
6	1·2	1·8	2·4	3	3·6	4·2	4·8	5·4	6	6·6	7·2
7	1·4	2·1	2·8	3·5	4·2	4·9	5·6	6·3	7	7·7	8·4
8	1·6	2·4	3·2	4	4·8	5·6	6·4	7·2	8	8·8	9·6
9	1·8	2·7	3·6	4·5	5·4	6·3	7·2	8·1	9	9·9	10·8
10	2	3	4	5	6	7	8	9	10	11	12
11	2·2	3·3	4·4	5·5	6·6	7·7	8·8	9·9	11	12·1	13·2
12	2·4	3·6	4·8	6	7·2	8·4	9·6	10·8	12	13·2	14·4

Fluency in Number Facts

Trios for the multiplication tables to 12 × 12

2 times table and related division facts

$1 \times 2 = 2$
$2 \times 1 = 2$
$2 \div 2 = 1$
$2 \div 1 = 2$

$2 \times 2 = 4$
$4 \div 2 = 2$

$3 \times 2 = 6$
$2 \times 3 = 6$
$6 \div 2 = 3$
$6 \div 3 = 2$

$4 \times 2 = 8$
$2 \times 4 = 8$
$8 \div 2 = 4$
$8 \div 4 = 2$

$5 \times 2 = 10$
$2 \times 5 = 10$
$10 \div 2 = 5$
$10 \div 5 = 2$

$6 \times 2 = 12$
$2 \times 6 = 12$
$12 \div 2 = 6$
$12 \div 6 = 2$

$7 \times 2 = 14$
$2 \times 7 = 14$
$14 \div 2 = 7$
$14 \div 7 = 2$

$8 \times 2 = 16$
$2 \times 8 = 16$
$16 \div 2 = 8$
$16 \div 8 = 2$

$9 \times 2 = 18$
$2 \times 9 = 18$
$18 \div 2 = 9$
$18 \div 9 = 2$

$10 \times 2 = 20$
$2 \times 10 = 20$
$20 \div 2 = 10$
$20 \div 10 = 2$

$11 \times 2 = 22$
$2 \times 11 = 22$
$22 \div 2 = 11$
$22 \div 11 = 2$

$12 \times 2 = 24$
$2 \times 12 = 24$
$24 \div 2 = 12$
$24 \div 12 = 2$

Fluency in Number Facts

3 times table and related division facts

$1 \times 3 = 3$
$3 \times 1 = 3$
$3 \div 3 = 1$
$3 \div 1 = 3$

$2 \times 3 = 6$
$3 \times 2 = 6$
$6 \div 3 = 2$
$6 \div 2 = 3$

$3 \times 3 = 9$
$9 \div 3 = 3$

$4 \times 3 = 12$
$3 \times 4 = 12$
$12 \div 3 = 4$
$12 \div 4 = 3$

$5 \times 3 = 15$
$3 \times 5 = 15$
$15 \div 3 = 5$
$15 \div 5 = 3$

$6 \times 3 = 18$
$3 \times 6 = 18$
$18 \div 3 = 6$
$18 \div 6 = 3$

$7 \times 3 = 21$
$3 \times 7 = 21$
$21 \div 3 = 7$
$21 \div 7 = 3$

$8 \times 3 = 24$
$3 \times 8 = 24$
$24 \div 3 = 8$
$24 \div 8 = 3$

$9 \times 3 = 27$
$3 \times 9 = 27$
$27 \div 3 = 9$
$27 \div 9 = 3$

$10 \times 3 = 30$
$3 \times 10 = 30$
$30 \div 3 = 10$
$30 \div 10 = 3$

$11 \times 3 = 33$
$3 \times 11 = 33$
$33 \div 3 = 11$
$33 \div 11 = 3$

$12 \times 3 = 36$
$3 \times 12 = 36$
$36 \div 3 = 12$
$36 \div 12 = 3$

Fluency in Number Facts

4 times table and related division facts

$1 \times 4 = 4$
$4 \times 1 = 4$
$4 \div 4 = 1$
$4 \div 1 = 4$

$2 \times 4 = 8$
$4 \times 2 = 8$
$8 \div 4 = 2$
$8 \div 2 = 4$

$3 \times 4 = 12$
$4 \times 3 = 12$
$12 \div 4 = 3$
$12 \div 3 = 4$

$4 \times 4 = 16$
$16 \div 4 = 4$

$5 \times 4 = 20$
$4 \times 5 = 20$
$20 \div 4 = 5$
$20 \div 5 = 4$

$6 \times 4 = 24$
$4 \times 6 = 24$
$24 \div 4 = 6$
$24 \div 6 = 4$

$7 \times 4 = 28$
$4 \times 7 = 28$
$28 \div 4 = 7$
$28 \div 7 = 4$

$8 \times 4 = 32$
$4 \times 8 = 32$
$32 \div 4 = 8$
$32 \div 8 = 4$

$9 \times 4 = 36$
$4 \times 9 = 36$
$36 \div 4 = 9$
$36 \div 9 = 4$

$10 \times 4 = 40$
$4 \times 10 = 40$
$40 \div 4 = 10$
$40 \div 10 = 4$

$11 \times 4 = 44$
$4 \times 11 = 44$
$44 \div 4 = 11$
$44 \div 11 = 4$

$12 \times 4 = 48$
$4 \times 12 = 48$
$48 \div 4 = 12$
$48 \div 12 = 4$

5 times table and related division facts

$1 \times 5 = 5$
$5 \times 1 = 5$
$5 \div 5 = 1$
$5 \div 1 = 5$

$2 \times 5 = 10$
$5 \times 2 = 10$
$10 \div 5 = 2$
$10 \div 2 = 5$

$3 \times 5 = 15$
$5 \times 3 = 15$
$15 \div 5 = 3$
$15 \div 3 = 5$

$4 \times 5 = 20$
$5 \times 4 = 20$
$20 \div 5 = 4$
$20 \div 4 = 5$

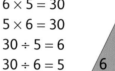

$5 \times 5 = 25$
$25 \div 5 = 5$

$6 \times 5 = 30$
$5 \times 6 = 30$
$30 \div 5 = 6$
$30 \div 6 = 5$

$7 \times 5 = 35$
$5 \times 7 = 35$
$35 \div 5 = 7$
$35 \div 7 = 5$

$8 \times 5 = 40$
$5 \times 8 = 40$
$40 \div 5 = 8$
$40 \div 8 = 5$

$9 \times 5 = 45$
$5 \times 9 = 45$
$45 \div 5 = 9$
$45 \div 9 = 5$

$10 \times 5 = 50$
$5 \times 10 = 50$
$50 \div 5 = 10$
$50 \div 10 = 5$

$11 \times 5 = 55$
$5 \times 11 = 55$
$55 \div 5 = 11$
$55 \div 11 = 5$

$12 \times 5 = 60$
$5 \times 12 = 60$
$60 \div 5 = 12$
$60 \div 12 = 5$

6 times table and related division facts

$1 \times 6 = 6$
$6 \times 1 = 6$
$6 \div 6 = 1$
$6 \div 1 = 6$

$2 \times 6 = 12$
$6 \times 2 = 12$
$12 \div 6 = 2$
$12 \div 2 = 6$

$3 \times 6 = 18$
$6 \times 3 = 18$
$18 \div 6 = 3$
$18 \div 3 = 6$

$4 \times 6 = 24$
$6 \times 4 = 24$
$24 \div 6 = 4$
$24 \div 4 = 6$

$5 \times 6 = 30$
$6 \times 5 = 30$
$30 \div 6 = 5$
$30 \div 5 = 6$

$6 \times 6 = 36$
$36 \div 6 = 6$

$7 \times 6 = 42$
$6 \times 7 = 42$
$42 \div 6 = 7$
$42 \div 7 = 6$

$8 \times 6 = 48$
$6 \times 8 = 48$
$48 \div 6 = 8$
$48 \div 8 = 6$

$9 \times 6 = 54$
$6 \times 9 = 54$
$54 \div 6 = 9$
$54 \div 9 = 6$

$10 \times 6 = 60$
$6 \times 10 = 60$
$60 \div 6 = 10$
$60 \div 10 = 6$

$11 \times 6 = 66$
$6 \times 11 = 66$
$66 \div 6 = 11$
$66 \div 11 = 6$

$12 \times 6 = 72$
$6 \times 12 = 72$
$72 \div 6 = 12$
$72 \div 12 = 6$

7 times table and related division facts

$1 \times 7 = 7$
$7 \times 1 = 7$
$7 \div 7 = 1$
$7 \div 1 = 7$

$2 \times 7 = 14$
$7 \times 2 = 14$
$14 \div 7 = 2$
$14 \div 2 = 7$

$3 \times 7 = 21$
$7 \times 3 = 21$
$21 \div 7 = 3$
$21 \div 3 = 7$

$4 \times 7 = 28$
$7 \times 4 = 28$
$28 \div 7 = 4$
$28 \div 4 = 7$

$5 \times 7 = 35$
$7 \times 5 = 35$
$35 \div 7 = 5$
$35 \div 5 = 7$

$6 \times 7 = 42$
$7 \times 6 = 42$
$42 \div 7 = 6$
$42 \div 6 = 7$

$7 \times 7 = 49$
$49 \div 7 = 7$

$8 \times 7 = 56$
$7 \times 8 = 56$
$56 \div 7 = 8$
$56 \div 8 = 7$

$9 \times 7 = 63$
$7 \times 9 = 63$
$63 \div 7 = 9$
$63 \div 9 = 7$

$10 \times 7 = 70$
$7 \times 10 = 70$
$70 \div 7 = 10$
$70 \div 10 = 7$

$11 \times 7 = 77$
$7 \times 11 = 77$
$77 \div 7 = 11$
$77 \div 11 = 7$

$12 \times 7 = 84$
$7 \times 12 = 84$
$84 \div 7 = 12$
$84 \div 12 = 7$

8 times table and related division facts

$1 \times 8 = 8$
$8 \times 1 = 8$
$8 \div 8 = 1$
$8 \div 1 = 8$

$2 \times 8 = 16$
$8 \times 2 = 16$
$16 \div 8 = 2$
$16 \div 2 = 8$

$3 \times 8 = 24$
$8 \times 3 = 24$
$24 \div 8 = 3$
$24 \div 3 = 8$

$4 \times 8 = 32$
$8 \times 4 = 32$
$32 \div 8 = 4$
$32 \div 4 = 8$

$5 \times 8 = 40$
$8 \times 5 = 40$
$40 \div 8 = 5$
$40 \div 5 = 8$

$6 \times 8 = 48$
$8 \times 6 = 48$
$48 \div 8 = 6$
$48 \div 6 = 8$

$7 \times 8 = 56$
$8 \times 7 = 56$
$56 \div 8 = 7$
$56 \div 7 = 8$

$8 \times 8 = 64$
$64 \div 8 = 8$

$9 \times 8 = 72$
$8 \times 9 = 72$
$72 \div 8 = 9$
$72 \div 9 = 8$

$10 \times 8 = 80$
$8 \times 10 = 80$
$80 \div 8 = 10$
$80 \div 10 = 8$

$11 \times 8 = 88$
$8 \times 11 = 88$
$88 \div 8 = 11$
$88 \div 11 = 8$

$12 \times 8 = 96$
$8 \times 12 = 96$
$96 \div 8 = 12$
$96 \div 12 = 8$

9 times table and related division facts

$1 \times 9 = 9$
$9 \times 1 = 9$
$9 \div 9 = 1$
$9 \div 1 = 9$

$2 \times 9 = 18$
$9 \times 2 = 18$
$18 \div 9 = 2$
$18 \div 2 = 9$

$3 \times 9 = 27$
$9 \times 3 = 27$
$27 \div 9 = 3$
$27 \div 3 = 9$

$4 \times 9 = 36$
$9 \times 4 = 36$
$36 \div 9 = 4$
$36 \div 4 = 9$

$5 \times 9 = 45$
$9 \times 5 = 45$
$45 \div 9 = 5$
$45 \div 5 = 9$

$6 \times 9 = 54$
$9 \times 6 = 54$
$54 \div 9 = 6$
$54 \div 6 = 9$

$7 \times 9 = 63$
$9 \times 7 = 63$
$63 \div 9 = 7$
$63 \div 7 = 9$

$8 \times 9 = 72$
$9 \times 8 = 72$
$72 \div 9 = 8$
$72 \div 8 = 9$

$9 \times 9 = 81$
$81 \div 9 = 9$

$10 \times 9 = 90$
$9 \times 10 = 90$
$90 \div 9 = 10$
$90 \div 10 = 9$

$11 \times 9 = 99$
$9 \times 11 = 99$
$99 \div 9 = 11$
$99 \div 11 = 9$

$12 \times 9 = 108$
$9 \times 12 = 108$
$108 \div 9 = 12$
$108 \div 12 = 9$

10 times table and related division facts

$1 \times 10 = 10$
$10 \times 1 = 10$
$10 \div 10 = 1$
$10 \div 1 = 10$

10
1   10

$2 \times 10 = 20$
$10 \times 2 = 20$
$20 \div 10 = 2$
$20 \div 2 = 10$

20
2   10

$3 \times 10 = 30$
$10 \times 3 = 30$
$30 \div 10 = 3$
$30 \div 3 = 10$

30
3   10

$4 \times 10 = 40$
$10 \times 4 = 40$
$40 \div 10 = 4$
$40 \div 4 = 10$

40
4   10

$5 \times 10 = 50$
$10 \times 5 = 50$
$50 \div 10 = 5$
$50 \div 5 = 10$

50
5   10

$6 \times 10 = 60$
$10 \times 6 = 60$
$60 \div 10 = 6$
$60 \div 6 = 10$

60
6   10

$7 \times 10 = 70$
$10 \times 7 = 70$
$70 \div 10 = 7$
$70 \div 7 = 10$

70
7   10

$8 \times 10 = 80$
$10 \times 8 = 80$
$80 \div 10 = 8$
$80 \div 8 = 10$

80
8   10

$9 \times 10 = 90$
$10 \times 9 = 90$
$90 \div 10 = 9$
$90 \div 9 = 10$

90
9   10

$10 \times 10 = 100$
$100 \div 10 = 10$

100
10   10

$11 \times 10 = 110$
$10 \times 11 = 110$
$110 \div 10 = 11$
$110 \div 11 = 10$

110
11   10

$12 \times 10 = 120$
$10 \times 12 = 120$
$120 \div 10 = 12$
$120 \div 12 = 10$

120
12   10

11 times table and related division facts

$1 \times 11 = 11$
$11 \times 1 = 11$
$11 \div 11 = 1$
$11 \div 1 = 11$

11 / 1   11

$2 \times 11 = 22$
$11 \times 2 = 22$
$22 \div 11 = 2$
$22 \div 2 = 11$

22 / 2   11

$3 \times 11 = 33$
$11 \times 3 = 33$
$33 \div 11 = 3$
$33 \div 3 = 11$

33 / 3   11

$4 \times 11 = 44$
$11 \times 4 = 44$
$44 \div 11 = 4$
$44 \div 4 = 11$

44 / 4   11

$5 \times 11 = 55$
$11 \times 5 = 55$
$55 \div 11 = 5$
$55 \div 5 = 11$

55 / 5   11

$6 \times 11 = 66$
$11 \times 6 = 66$
$66 \div 11 = 6$
$66 \div 6 = 11$

66 / 6   11

$7 \times 11 = 77$
$11 \times 7 = 77$
$77 \div 11 = 7$
$77 \div 7 = 11$

77 / 7   11

$8 \times 11 = 88$
$11 \times 8 = 88$
$88 \div 11 = 8$
$88 \div 8 = 11$

88 / 8   11

$9 \times 11 = 99$
$11 \times 9 = 99$
$99 \div 11 = 9$
$99 \div 9 = 11$

99 / 9   11

$10 \times 11 = 110$
$11 \times 10 = 110$
$110 \div 11 = 10$
$110 \div 10 = 11$

110 / 10   11

$11 \times 11 = 121$
$121 \div 11 = 11$

121 / 11   11

$12 \times 11 = 132$
$11 \times 12 = 132$
$132 \div 11 = 12$
$132 \div 12 = 11$

132 / 12   11

12 times table and related division facts

$1 \times 12 = 12$
$12 \times 1 = 12$
$12 \div 12 = 1$
$12 \div 1 = 12$

12
1   12

$2 \times 12 = 24$
$12 \times 2 = 24$
$24 \div 12 = 2$
$24 \div 2 = 12$

24
2   12

$3 \times 12 = 36$
$12 \times 3 = 36$
$36 \div 12 = 3$
$36 \div 3 = 12$

36
3   12

$4 \times 12 = 48$
$12 \times 4 = 48$
$48 \div 12 = 4$
$48 \div 4 = 12$

48
4   12

$5 \times 12 = 60$
$12 \times 5 = 60$
$60 \div 12 = 5$
$60 \div 5 = 12$

60
5   12

$6 \times 12 = 72$
$12 \times 6 = 72$
$72 \div 12 = 6$
$72 \div 6 = 12$

72
6   12

$7 \times 12 = 84$
$12 \times 7 = 84$
$84 \div 12 = 7$
$84 \div 7 = 12$

84
7   12

$8 \times 12 = 96$
$12 \times 8 = 96$
$96 \div 12 = 8$
$96 \div 8 = 12$

96
8   12

$9 \times 12 = 108$
$12 \times 9 = 108$
$108 \div 12 = 9$
$108 \div 9 = 12$

108
9   12

$10 \times 12 = 120$
$12 \times 10 = 120$
$120 \div 12 = 10$
$120 \div 10 = 12$

120
10   12

$11 \times 12 = 132$
$12 \times 11 = 132$
$132 \div 12 = 11$
$132 \div 11 = 12$

132
11   12

$12 \times 12 = 144$
$144 \div 12 = 12$

144
12   12

Read, order and compare numbers at least to 1 000 000

Scientific comparisons
A game for 2 players

You need:
- 4 counters: 2 of one colour, 2 of another colour
- 2 buttons: 1 for each player
- pencil and paperclip (for the spinner)

Before you start:
- Decide who will have which colour counters.
- Decide who is Player 1 and who is Player 2.
- Put the buttons at the bottom of each thermometer.

What to do :
- Each player puts one of their counters on any bottle.
- Each player then puts their other counter on another bottle.
- One player spins the spinner.
- Follow the spinner's instructions.
- The winner (or winners) move their button up the thermometer.
- Remove the counters from the bottles.
- Repeat the above.

The winner is:
- the first player to score 10 points on their thermometer.

> Be sure not to cover the numbers.

largest number wins 1 point

smallest number wins 1 point

two numbers in between win 1 point each

🔑 Read numbers at least to 1 000 000 and determine the value of each digit

Stone age value
A game for 2 players

You need:
- 24 counters: 12 of one colour, 12 of another colour
- pencil and paperclip (for the spinner)

Before you start:
- Decide who will have which colour counters.
- Take turns to put one of your counters on a stone tablet until all 24 tablets have a counter on them.

> Be sure not to cover the numbers.

Take turns to:
- spin the spinner
- look at all the tablets with one of your counters on them, and if one of these numbers has a digit with the same place value as the number spun, remove your counter from the tablet.

Golden rule
- You can only remove one counter from one tablet each spin.

The winner is:
- the first player to remove all the counters from their 12 tablets.

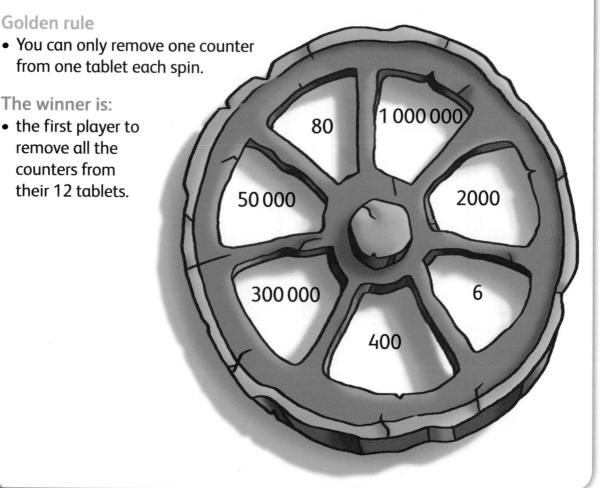

🔑 Identify the value of each digit to three decimal places

🔑 Read and compare numbers with up to three decimal places

Cupcake value
A game for 2 players

You need:
- 24 counters: 12 of one colour, 12 of another colour
- pencil and paperclip (for the spinner)

Before you start:
- Decide who will have which colour counters.
- Take turns to put one of your counters on a cupcake until all 24 cupcakes have a counter on them.

> Be sure not to cover the numbers.

Take turns to:
- spin the pink spinner
- look at all the cupcakes with one of your counters on them, and if one of these decimals has a digit with the same place value as the spinner value, remove your counter from the cupcake.

Golden rule
- You can only remove a counter from one cupcake each spin.

The winner is:
- the first player to remove all the counters from their 12 cupcakes.

Cupcake comparisons
A game for 2 players

You need:
- about 15 counters
- pencil and paperclip (for the spinner)

Take turns to:
- spin the chocolate spinner
- find a decimal on the cupcakes that fits the description
- cover the decimal with a counter.

The winner is:
- the first player to complete a line of 4 counters. A line can go sideways ↔, up and down ↕, or diagonally ↘.

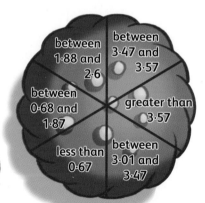

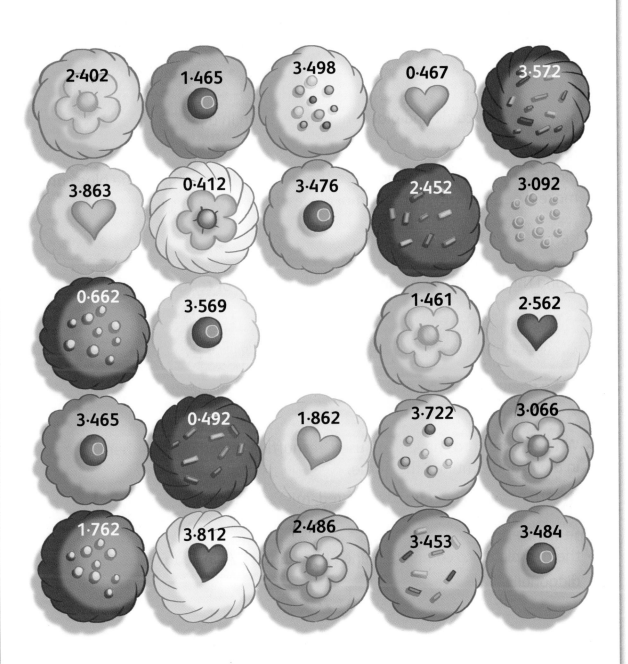

Round decimals with two decimal places to the nearest whole number and to one decimal place

Whirlpool rounding
A game for 2 players

You need:
- 2 × 1–9 number cards
- about 30 counters

Before you start:
- Shuffle all the cards and place them face down in a pile.

Take turns to:
- pick the top three cards and place them from left to right, on the blue cards to make a decimal with two decimal places, for example:

6 • 5 3

- round the number to the nearest whole number or tenth

> 6·53 rounded to the nearest tenth is 6·5.

> 6·53 rounded to the nearest whole number is 7.

- place a counter on the grid on the number you rounded to.

Golden rules
- When all the cards have been used, reshuffle the cards, place them face down in a pile and continue the game.
- If both numbers are already covered, miss that turn.

The winner is:
- the first player to complete a line of 4 counters. A line can go across ⟷ or diagonally ↘.

0·1	0·2	0·3	0·4	0·5	0·6	0·7	0·8	0·9	1
1·1	1·2	1·3	1·4	1·5	1·6	1·7	1·8	1·9	2
2·1	2·2	2·3	2·4	2·5	2·6	2·7	2·8	2·9	3
3·1	3·2	3·3	3·4	3·5	3·6	3·7	3·8	3·9	4
4·1	4·2	4·3	4·4	4·5	4·6	4·7	4·8	4·9	5
5·1	5·2	5·3	5·4	5·5	5·6	5·7	5·8	5·9	6
6·1	6·2	6·3	6·4	6·5	6·6	6·7	6·8	6·9	7
7·1	7·2	7·3	7·4	7·5	7·6	7·7	7·8	7·9	8
8·1	8·2	8·3	8·4	8·5	8·6	8·7	8·8	8·9	9
9·1	9·2	9·3	9·4	9·5	9·6	9·7	9·8	9·9	10

Multiply and divide whole numbers by 10, 100 and 1000

Anyone for tennis?
A game for 2 players

You need:
- button
- pencil and paperclip (for the spinner)
- about 30 counters

Take turns to:
- choose a number from the tennis rackets and put the button on the racket
- spin the spinner
- perform the calculation, saying the number sentence
- cover the answer on the tennis balls.

Golden rule
- If the answer is not on a tennis ball or is already covered, miss that turn.

The winner is:
- the first player to complete a line of 4 counters. A line can go across ⟷, up and down ↕, or diagonally ↘.

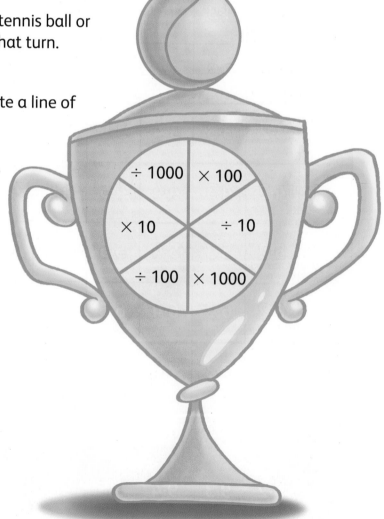

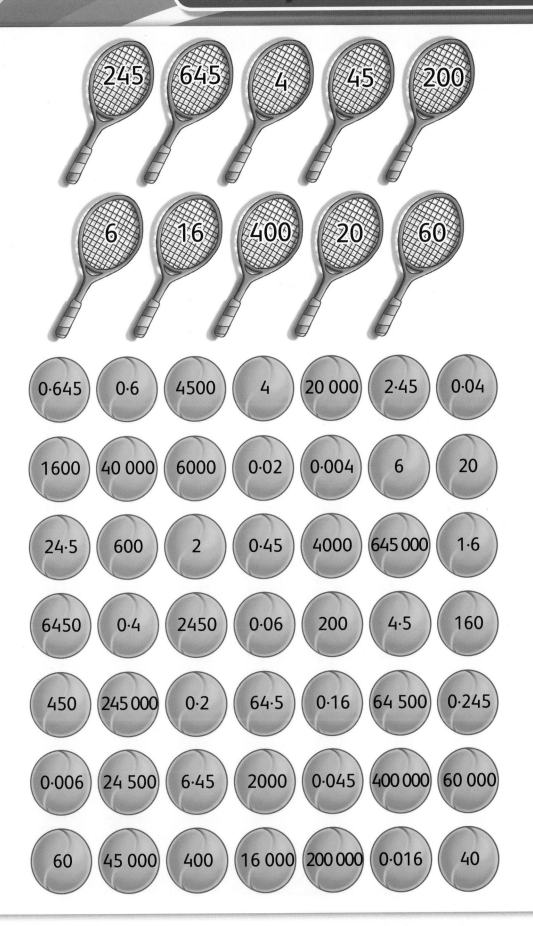

Multiply and divide numbers by 10 and 100 where the answers are up to three decimal places

A night at the opera
A game for 2 players

You need:
- button
- pencil and paperclip (for the spinner)
- 10 counters

Take turns to:
- choose a number from one of the singers and put the button on the singer
- spin the spinner
- perform the calculation, saying the number sentence
- look for the answer on the chairs.

- If the answer is on a chair with a star on it, take a counter.

The winner is:
- the first player to collect 5 counters.

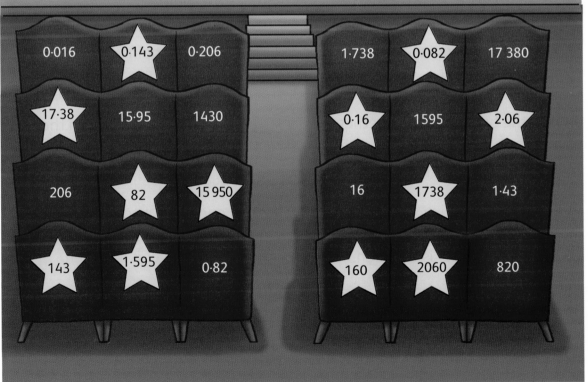

Add and subtract mentally two 2-digit numbers

Animal range – Addition
A game for 2 players

You need:
- 2 × 0–9 dice
- 12 counters: 6 of one colour, 6 of another colour

Before you start:
- Decide who will have which colour counters.

Take turns to:
- roll both dice to make a 2-digit number

- roll both dice again to make another 2-digit number

- add the two numbers together and say the answer

> 53 add 82 is 135.

- place one of your counters on the animal that shows the number range that their answer is between.

The winner is:
- the first player to put their counters on 6 different animals.

Animal range – Subtraction
A game for 2 players

You need:
- 2 × 0–9 dice
- 10 counters: 5 of one colour, 5 of another colour

Before you start:
- Decide who will have which colour counters.

Take turns to:
- roll both dice to make a 2-digit number

- roll both dice again to make another 2-digit number

- find the difference between the two numbers and say the answer

> 85 subtract 23 is 62.

- place one of your counters on the animal that shows the number range that their answer is between.

The winner is:
- the first player to put their counters on 5 different animals.

Hint
Think carefully about how you're going to arrange the dice to make your 2-digit numbers.

1–20

21–40

41–60

61–80

81–100

101–120

121–140

141–160

161–180

181–200

57

🔑 Add mentally multiples of 100 and 1000

Roman additions
A game for 2 players

You need:
- 2 × 1–6 dice
- 2 buttons
- coin
- 12 counters

Take turns to:

- roll both dice

- cover the matching dice numbers (one above the Roman head and one above the column) with buttons

- add the two numbers (one on the Roman head and one on the column) together and say the answer.

When both players have had a turn, one player tosses the coin.

Golden rule

heads	tails

larger answer wins · smaller answer wins

The winner of that round takes a counter.

The winner is:
- the player with more counters after 12 rounds.

3059

4513

2802

7936

6348

5372

4000

800

1600

2000

500

5200

Fluency in Number Facts

🗝️ Subtract mentally multiples of 100 and 1000

Helicopters and buses
A game for 2 players

You need:
- 2 × 1–6 dice
- 2 buttons
- coin
- 12 counters

Take turns to:
- roll both dice
- cover the matching dice numbers (one above the helicopter and one above the bus) with buttons
- find the difference between the two numbers (one on the helicopter and one on the bus) and say the answer.

When both players have had a turn, one player tosses the coin.

Golden rule

heads   tails

larger answer wins   smaller answer wins

The winner of that round takes a counter.

The winner is:
- the player with more counters after 12 rounds.

Add and subtract mentally a 2-digit number to or from a 3-digit number

Sunflower sums – Addition
A game for 2 players

Before you start:
- Decide who will have which button.
- Put the two buttons on the queen bee at the top of the page.

You need:
- 2 different buttons: 1 for each player
- 12 counters
- 2 × 1–6 dice: 1 for each player
- pencil and paper (optional)

YOU CAN USE PENCIL AND PAPER TO HELP YOU WORK OUT THE ANSWER.

What to do:
- One player puts one of the counters on a sunflower.
- Each player rolls their dice and moves their button clockwise that number of bees.

Be sure not to cover the number.

- Each player then adds their 2-digit bee number to the 3-digit sunflower number.
- Players then share their answers.
- The player whose answer is closest to a multiple of 100, wins that round and keeps the counter.
- Play 12 rounds.

Golden rule
- If both players land on the same bee together, both players roll their dice again.

The winner is:
- the player with more counters after 12 rounds.

Variation:

Sunflower sums – Subtraction
- Each player subtracts their 2-digit bee number from the 3-digit sunflower number.

Fluency in Number Facts

Add and subtract decimals mentally: U·t ± U·t

Explorer's map – Addition
A game for 2 players

You need:
- 2 × 1–6 dice
- 2 buttons
- 12 counters

Take turns to:
- roll both dice, for example 3 and 6, and use the numbers as coordinates, i.e. (3, 6) gives 0·7
- place a button in the square with that decimal
- roll both dice again to get another decimal
- place a button in the square with this decimal
- add the two decimals together.

> Be sure not to cover the decimals.

The player with the larger answer wins that round and takes a counter.

The winner is:
- the player with more counters after 12 rounds.

Variation

Explorer's map – Subtraction
- Players find the difference between the two decimals.
- The player with the larger difference wins the round.

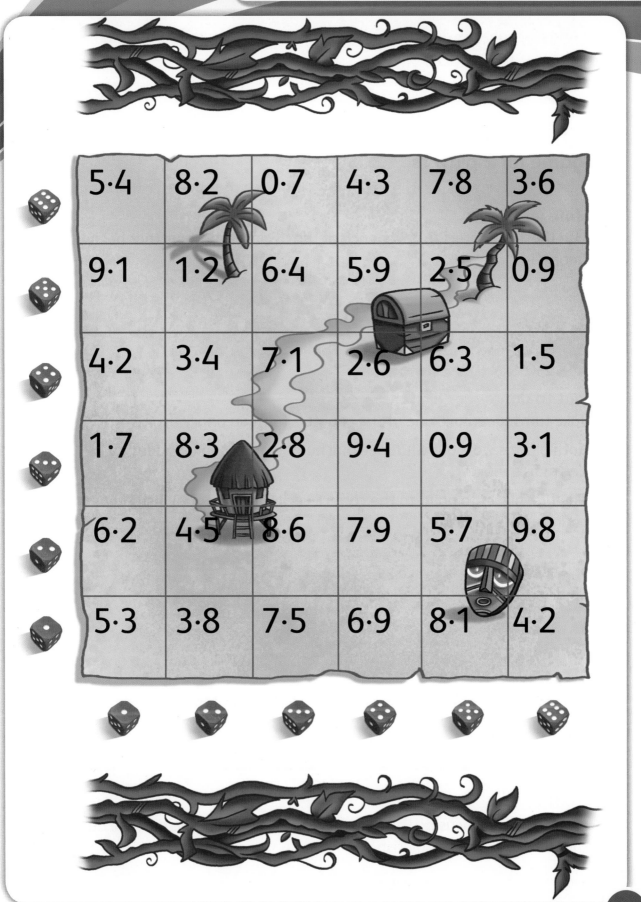

5·4	8·2	0·7	4·3	7·8	3·6
9·1	1·2	6·4	5·9	2·5	0·9
4·2	3·4	7·1	2·6	6·3	1·5
1·7	8·3	2·8	9·4	0·9	3·1
6·2	4·5	8·6	7·9	5·7	9·8
5·3	3·8	7·5	6·9	8·1	4·2

Add and subtract decimals mentally, including calculating complements of 1, e.g. 0·83 + 0·17

Fishing for 1
A game for 2 players

You need:
- 14 counters

Before you start:
- Use the 14 counters to cover each of the decimal numbers that belong to the angry fish.

What to do:
- Take turns to remove one of the counters from an angry fish.
- Both players work out what decimal number needs to be added to the decimal to make 1.
- The first player to point to the correct decimal on a happy fish keeps the counter, for example:

The winner is:
- the player with more counters after all 14 counters have been removed from the angry fish.

Variation
- Start the game by using the counters to cover each of the decimal numbers that belong to the happy fish.

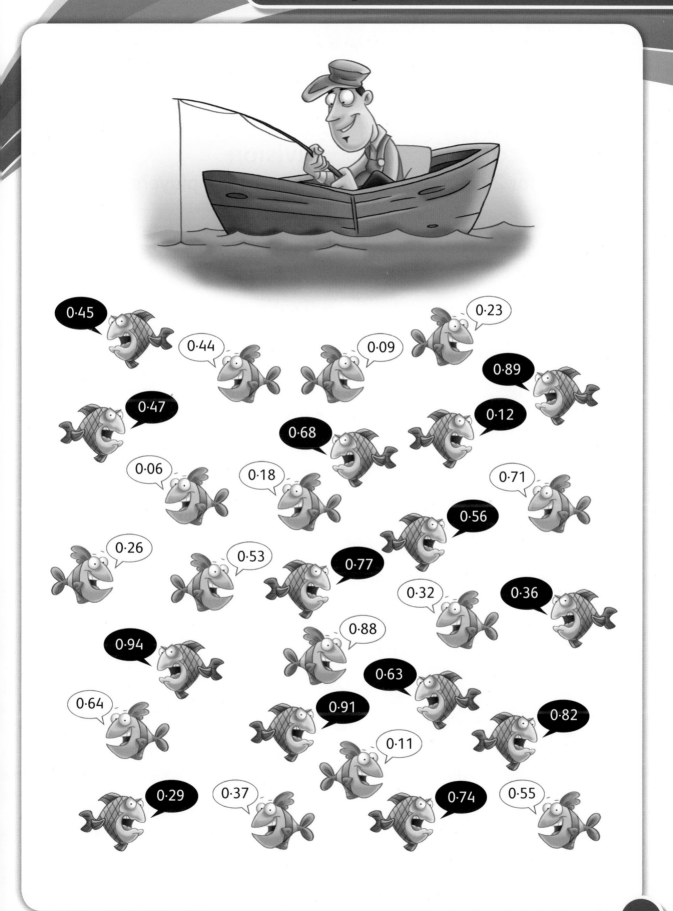

🔑 Recall multiplication and division facts for multiplication tables up to 12 × 12

Swimming pool – Multiplication
A game for 2 players

You need:
- 2 different buttons: 1 for each player

Before you start:
- Decide who will have which button.

Take turns to:
- roll the dice twice
- multiply the two numbers together
- find the answer in the swimming pool and put your button on that number.

> 4 times 10 is 40.

> 12 times 6 is 72.

The player whose number is nearer the finishing line wins that round and takes a counter.

> 40 is closer than 72 to the finishing line.

6	15	28	35	42	84	40	63	30	88	48
2	30	4	10	30	77	24	27	120	22	144
10	3	48	25	12	14	96	72	80	110	36
24	33	44	55	66	42	56	9	20	99	108

Golden rule
- If both players are the same distance from the finishing line, each player takes a counter.

Swimming pool – Division
A game for 2 players

- 1–12 dice
- 20 counters

Take turns to:
- roll the dice

> If you roll 1, roll the dice again.

- find that lane on the swimming pool and put your button on the starting block
- roll the dice again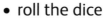
- count up the lane that many numbers
- divide this number by the lane number.

> 72 divided by 6 is 12.

The player with the larger answer wins that round and takes a counter.

Golden rule
- If both players get the same answer, each player takes a counter.

The winner is:
- the player with more counters after 20 rounds.

6	15	28	35	42	84	40	63	30	88	48
2	30	4	10	30	77	24	27	120	22	144
10	3	48	25	12	14	96	72	80	110	36
24	33	44	55	66	42	56	9	20	99	108
12	18	24	40	54	21	8	99	110	33	24
8	12	16	5	36	63	72	54	70	132	12
14	24	40	20	48	7	16	36	40	44	72
20	6	32	50	24	35	88	18	90	77	120
4	27	12	15	72	56	48	81	10	121	60
16	9	20	30	6	49	80	90	60	11	84
18	21	36	60	18	70	64	108	100	55	132
22	36	8	45	60	28	32	45	50	66	96
2	3	4	5	6	7	8	9	10	11	12

Multiply multiples of 10 and 100 by a one-digit number mentally, drawing upon known multiplication facts

A day at the beach – Multiples of 10
A game for 2 players

You need:
- 0–9 dice
- pencil and paperclip (for the spinner)
- 12 counters

Before you start:
- Use the blue umbrella and blue beach ball spinner.
- Decide who will have the numbers on the blue strips of the umbrella and who will have the numbers on the white strips.

Take turns to:
- roll the dice (if you roll 0 or 1, roll the dice again)
- spin the beach ball spinner
- multiply the two numbers together and say the calculation.

If the answer is one of the numbers on your umbrella strips, cover the number with a counter.

The winner is:
- the first player to cover 6 of their numbers on the umbrella.

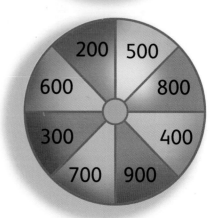

Variation

A day at the beach – Multiples of 100
- Use the red umbrella and red beach ball spinner.
- Decide who will have the numbers on the red strips of the umbrella and who will have the numbers on the white strips.

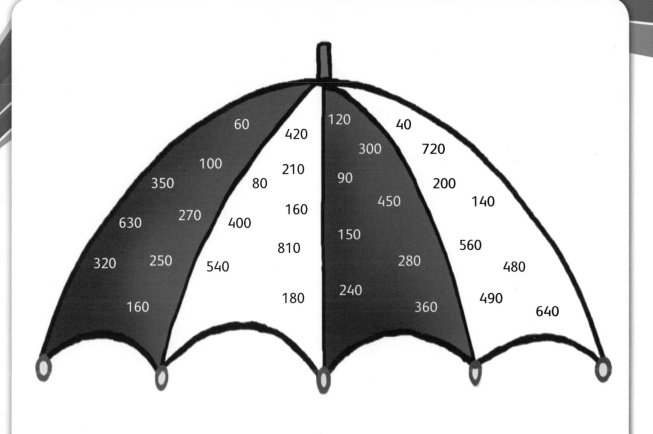

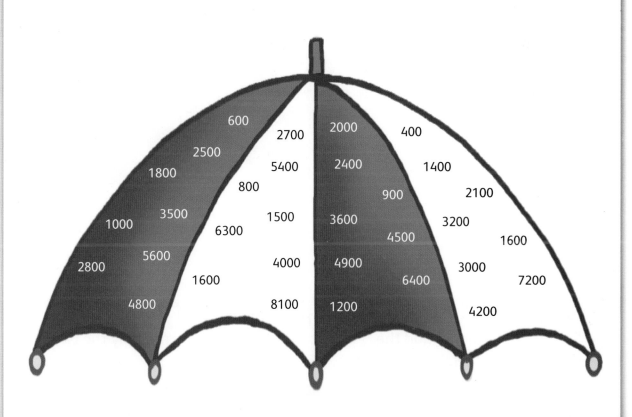

Multiply pairs of multiples of 10 and 100 mentally, drawing upon known multiplication facts

Multiples of Australia – Multiples of 10
A game for 2 players

You need:
- pencil and paper clip (for the spinner)
- 16 counters: 8 of one colour, 8 of another colour

Before you start:
- Decide who will have which colour counters.

Take turns to:
- spin the sun spinner twice
- multiply the two numbers together
- say the calculation
- cover the Australian landmark at the top of the page that shows the answer.

The winner is:
- the first player to put 2 of their counters on each of the 4 landmarks.

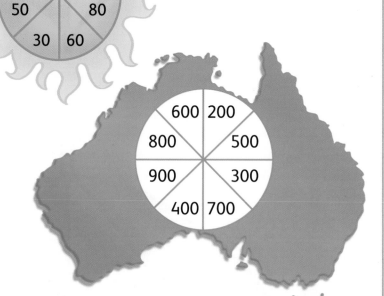

Variation

Multiples of Australia – Multiples of 10 and 100

- Spin the sun spinner and the Australian map spinner and multiply the two numbers together.
- Cover the Australian animal at the bottom of the page that shows the answer.
- The winner is the first player to put 2 of their counters on each of the 4 animals.

Sydney Opera House
600, 1800, 2000, 2500, 2700, 3500, 5400, 7200

Uluru (Ayres Rock)
400, 1000, 1500, 3200, 3600, 4200, 4900, 8100

Sydney Harbour Bridge
800, 1600, 2100, 2400, 3000, 4000, 5600, 6400

Great Barrier Reef
900, 1200, 1400, 2400, 2800, 4500, 4800, 6300

Kangaroo
9000, 14 000, 16 000, 24 000, 35 000, 40 000, 64 000, 72 000

Emu
6000, 18 000, 21 000, 28 000, 30 000, 45 000, 48 000, 63 000

Koala
4000, 12 000, 15 000, 25 000, 36 000, 42 000, 48 000, 49 000

Wombat
8000, 10 000, 20 000, 27 000, 32 000, 54 000, 56 000, 81 000

Multiply a 2-digit number by a 1-digit number

Movie time
A game for 2 players

You need:
- 12 counters
- 0–9 dice
- coin
- pencil and paper (optional)

Before you start:
- Cover any 12 movie numbers with a counter.

Take turns to:
- remove a counter
- roll the dice (if you roll 0 or 1, roll the dice again)
- multiply the movie number by the dice number and say the calculation.

YOU CAN USE PENCIL AND PAPER TO HELP YOU WORK OUT THE ANSWER.

When both players have had a turn, one player tosses the coin.

Golden rule

heads  tails

larger answer wins   smaller answer wins

The winner takes both counters removed from the movie numbers.

The winner is:
- the player with more counters once all 12 counters have been removed from the movie numbers.

36	64	76	42	28
79	93	98	51	14
89	67	87	65	31
84	38	56	17	49
82	53	25	73	91
24	72	19	45	63

Divide a 2-digit number by a 1-digit number

The remainders in the tower
A game for 2 players

You need:
- 12 counters
- 0–9 dice

Before you start:

- Cover any 12 of the 2-digit numbers with a counter.

- Decide who will have the remainders in the left tower and who will have the reminders in the right tower.

What to do:

- One player removes a counter.

- The other player rolls the dice.

- Work together to divide the 2-digit number by the dice number.

- Look at the remainder in the answer. The player who has that remainder in their tower keeps the counter.

Golden rules

- If you roll 0, divide by 10.

- If you roll 1, roll the dice again.

The winner is:

- the player with more counters after all 12 counters have been removed from the 2-digit numbers.

Multiply 1-digit numbers with up to two decimal places by whole numbers

Robot wars
A game for 2 players

You need:
- button
- 0–9 dice
- 10 counters
- pencil and paper (optional)

Before you start:
- Decide who is Player 1 and who is Player 2.

Take turns to:
- choose a number from one of the robots and put the button on the robot
- roll the dice (if you roll 0 or 1, roll the dice again)
- multiply the dice number by the number on the robot and say the calculation.

YOU CAN USE PENCIL AND PAPER TO HELP YOU WORK OUT THE ANSWER.

If the answer is one of the numbers on the grid, put a counter on the **other** player's laser.

The loser is:
- the first player with 5 counters on their laser.

Not all the answers are on the grid.

7·6	15	34·3	2·5	4·8	4·32
5·76	44·1	8	3·75	15·2	17·5
10	34·2	24·5	3·2	19·6	2·16
3·6	7·5	26·6	12·8	22·5	9·6

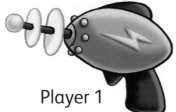

Player 1

Player 2

Resources used in *Fluency in Number Facts* Years 5 & 6

Key domain	Game	Pages	Counters	1–9 digit cards	Pencil and paperclip (for the spinner)	1–6 dice	0–9 dice	1–12 dice	Button	Coin	Pencil and paper
Number and place value	Scientific comparisons	44–45	•		•				•		
	Stone age value	46–47	•		•						
	Cupcake value Cupcake comparisons	48–49	•		•						
	Whirlpool rounding	50–51	•	•							
	Anyone for tennis?	52–53	•		•				•		
	A night at the opera	54–55	•		•				•		
Addition and subtraction	Animal range	56–57	•				•				
	Roman additions	58–59	•			•			•	•	
	Helicopters and buses	60–61	•			•			•	•	
	Sunflower sums	62–63	•			•			•		•
	Explorer's map	64–65	•			•			•		
	Fishing for 1	66–67	•								
Multiplication and division	Swimming pool	68–69	•					•	•		
	A day at the beach	70–71	•		•		•				
	Multiples of Australia	72–73	•		•						
	Movie time	74–75	•				•			•	•
	The remainders in the tower	76–77	•				•				
	Robot wars	78–79	•				•		•		•

How to use a spinner

Some of the paired games in this book require a spinner. This is easily made using a pencil, a paperclip and the spinner printed on each games page. Hold the paperclip in the centre of the spinner using the pencil and gently flick the paperclip with your finger to make it spin.